Martín Adán

THE CARDBOARD HOUSE

A new translation
by José Garay Boszeta

THE CARDBOARD HOUSE

Originally published in Perú in 1928 as *La Casa de Cartón*

Email: jose@dulzorada.com

Cover design and layout: Miguel Garay Boszeta
Email: miguel@dulzorada.com
Dulzorada logo design: Bidkar Yapo @nacion.chicha

ISBN-13: 978-0-578-69016-2
Published by Dulzorada.

Printed in the USA

Ramón Rafael de la Fuente Benavides, “Martín Adán”. Circa, 1930’s.

CONTENTS

Translator's Introduction

Lima, Perú. 1925. The young Ramón Rafael de la Fuente Benavides —a model student in the Deutsche Schule of Lima— walks through the fog on the streets of Barranco, towards a sunset that, as a triptych, breaks down the geographical limits between the sky, the earth and the sea. He is going to the seafront, so he would have to go across the square, past the colonial church that launches strokes of the bell to the wind at six in the afternoon, and then go across the ancient wooden bridge on which it is said that unrequited lovers gather every evening to sigh at the sundown. Ramón has always been a little nostalgic and contemplative, and maybe watching the sunsets while facing the sea —their warm half-light, their odors and colors— offer him that strange mixture of eternity and emptiness that always has concerned poets so much. Ramón, with his sixteen years of age, has already read some of the poems of his neighbor, José María Eguren. He has perceived in Eguren's poems something about the ghostly watercolor of his neighborhood, Barranco. He has had to read also the unavoidable Spanish classics of his bourgeois education. But he has also been able to read some Joyce, Whitman, Anatole France, a bit of Nietzsche, among others, and has begun to form his own opinions. His family must not know this, but his teachers and classmates believe that Ramón wants to be a poet. But he still doesn't know very well what he wants to be or to do with his sixteen years of age. Yet, Ramón has begun to write in his notebook. Encouraged above all by his professors Luis Alberto Sánchez (history) and Emilio Huidobro (grammar), both committed intellectuals who tell him and his closest friends (Estuardo Nuñez, Xavier Abril, Emilio Adolfo Westphalen) about the literary avant-garde and the winds of renewal in Latin America; about the image of César Vallejo, who has recently emigrated to Europe escaping from the spleen of Lima; about the friendly figure of José María Eguren who slowly ages amidst the humidity of the seaport. Ramón's curiosity has definitely grown. He has finished school, has met writers and poets, has started attending the literary gatherings in Eguren's house, and above all, he has continued writing in his notebook.

Now it's the year 1927. Since the past year, the cultural and literary scene in Lima has received an influx of vitality, driven by the immense energy of *Amauta* magazine and its director José Carlos Mariátegui. For the young writers, *Amauta* represented a much anticipated force of renewal, acting as the platform for a multiplicity of voices that were eagerly directing their gazes towards the future. Ramón is, to be sure, fed up of growing up with the discipline of Clericalism, with compulsive morality, with the conservatism of his family. He has made up his mind and decided to visit Mariátegui, and present himself with no other credentials than his clean shirt and his secret notebook. He has asked his friend Estuardo Nuñez, who is acquainted, to introduce him. Their first meeting could not have been more auspicious. Mariátegui, with the insight that characterized him, has immediately recognized the historical importance of Ramón's first sketches in his notebook, which by now had the working title of *"The Cardboard House"*, and therein he has seen the birth of a new style, one radically opposed to tradition and open to the experimental waves of the avant-garde. His response was immediate and unexpected. The *amauta*[1] Mariátegui has declared

[1]. Amauta is a word in the Quechua language that means "wise one" or "teacher". It was reserved for the elders and educators in the Inca Empire. Besides being the name of his publication, Mariátegui often received the sobriquet of amauta as a sign of deference by his sympathizers.

his unconditional support of Ramón's work, as well as the imminent publication of previews in *Amauta* magazine. There was only one remaining issue: the name of the author. For it happens that both Ramón and Mariátegui have very valid reasons to avoid using the author's proper name. Ramón is especially concerned with the potential reaction of his conservative relatives after seeing his prestigious family name associated with an immoral book, and to make matters worse, to see it published in a left-wing, socialist magazine. As far as Mariátegui is concerned, it seems to him absolutely inconceivable that an aristocratic name such as Ramón Rafael de la Fuente Benavides could correspond to a writing of such an experimental dislocation. It would be Mariátegui who, in an extended session with Ramón and Estuardo (acting as the conciliator of terms), formulates the problem:

— I have the impression that you visibly represent the persistent attempt to reach the complete transformation, the end of the strenous jump that goes from the ape to the man... We must look, therefore, for two terms that represent or symbolize this event.

After a series of searches and tests, Nuñez argued:

— In this case, representing the ape, we could use the word Martín... Almost all the monkeys I know are called Martín.

— Perfectly. —Continued the amauta— And since there are so many human sobriquets to represent our genre, we will take that of the first one to inhabit the earth: Adán.

— Perfectly. —exclaimed the three remaining fellows— Martín Adán.[2]

Thus, with barely eighteen years of age, Ramón Rafael de la Fuente Benavides died, and Martín Adán was born.

In order to understand the major event that the publication of *The Cardboard House* would come to represent in Latin American literature, it's necessary to contextualize its appearance within the cultural renaissance of Perú in the 1920's. During this decade, a multiplicity of political and intellectual groups proliferated everywhere in the continent. Influenced by the revolutionary currents of the times and facing a dire political situation, they maintained a close communication with each other, creating a vast cultural network of support and exchange of information. The *de facto* dictatorship of Augusto B. Leguía —the *oncenio* or the eleven years (1919-1930)—, had created a state of permanent agitation, coupled with an accelerated social

---

2. *Bazan, Armando (1902-1962). Mariátegui y Martín Adán. Cultura Perúana, No. 130. 1959.* Martín was purpotedly the most popular name for an organ grinder's monkey at the time.

transformation promoted by big international capitals, in addition to, of course, the vernacular corruption and systematic repression inherited from the old colonial regime. These were, undoubtedly, very intense times, to which the restless youth of the moment responded by fervently embracing the revolutionary ideals in all fields of expression; in political and social organization, as well as in literary and artistic creation. The result was the birth of a broad conception of the avant-garde that was not only limited to artistic creation, but that, in the pursuit of a conscious need for a political critique, fostered a demand for radically new expressions in all fields of social life. The avant-garde in Latin America, which found parallel developments in every country, must be conceived in retrospective as the movement in search for a total praxis in the public and the private spheres; a new morality that could respond to the challenges of Modernity and the demands of its novel social formations. What was brewing everywhere from North to South, from Mexico City to Buenos Aires, was the ferment of a new post-colonial spirit: a new subjectivity of what it meant to be Latin American in the Twentieth Century, a new identity that could integrate equally indigenous and cosmopolitan traditions into autonomous projects for the past, present and future of the continent. In regards to the Peruvian process, we must mention among these groups the Grupo del

Norte (or Bohemia Trujillana), which included among its ranks the likes of César Vallejo, Antenor Orrego and Víctor Raúl Haya de la Torre; the Orkopata Group of Puno, in southern Perú, with Gamaliel Churata as the publisher of the "indigenista and avant-garde" Titikaka Bulletin; and above all, in Lima, the circle of collaborators gravitating around *Amauta* magazine (1926-1930) and the figure of its editor-in-chief, José Carlos Mariátegui. It is not an exaggeration to say that *Amauta* and Mariátegui were in the eye of a generational storm that spearheaded a new and total conception of the avant-garde, organizing connections that transcended the national field and creating solid networks of exchange between Europe and Latin America. As it has been demonstrated in recent years by the research of the José Carlos Mariátegui Archive in Lima and the various international exhibitions centered around *Amauta* magazine[3], the brief existence of this publication remains as one of the most important cultural and intellectual experiences in Latin America, where seemingly heterogeneous currents (indigenism,

---

3. — Documentos en la mira. José Carlos Mariátegui archive. Lima, 2016. http://www.Mariátegui.org/exposiciones/documentos-en-la-mira/
— Un espiritu en movimiento. Casa de la Literatura Perúana. Lima, 2018. http://www.casadelaliteratura.gob.pe/tag/un-espiritu-en-movimiento/
— The Avant-garde networks of Amauta. Museo de Arte de Lima, Blanton Museum of Art. Madrid, Lima, Mexico City, Austin. 2019-2020. https://blantonmuseum.org/exhibition/amauta/

futurism, socialism, etc.) were found together for the first time in a coherent vision and a broad sense of praxis for the 20th century: An ethics, aesthetics and politics for the new identity and liberation of Latin America.

For Mariátegui, who was keenly aware of the implications of this process as it unfolded, the appearance —we could even say the revelation— of a character like Martín Adán represented one of the most interesting manifestations of the historical decline of traditional Peruvian society, of its colonial bourgeoisie in particular, always so utterly reactionary and conservative. In Mariátegui's view, Martín Adán and *The Cardboard House* were, first and foremost, the heralds of a new spirit, a prophecy of the imminent downfall and transformation of the ancient regime of colonial hegemony. Of course, it was not an accident that the swan song of the old social order was to be sung by the penmanship of one of the privileged sons of the ruling class. On the contrary, as is common during revolutionary periods, the articulations of decadence are usually well represented among those beneficiaries of the upper classes, whether they appear as articulated critiques of its excesses or as a pure exercise of its vices. *The Cardboard House* is, admittedly, a little of both, and that is why Mariátegui thought to see clearly in it the simultaneous announcement of an ending and a beginning. Hence, his fascination with the symbolic embodiment of two opposite essences: spirituality and corporeality, dogma and science, or Genesis and Darwin. Ergo, Martín Adán. We must consider to what extent the character of Martín Adán was composed as one of Mariátegui's many creative projects. By attributing to Adán the idea of an almost chimerical reconciliation of divergent terms, Mariátegui thought to articulate here, explicitly, a very significant synthesis. All these "dialectical" tensions could not have happened accidentally or go by unnoticed from the point of view of a "convicted and self-confessed" Marxist like José Carlos Mariátegui. Martín Adán was, to be sure, like most forcibly anointed prophets, a little uninvolved, somewhat indifferent, even completely unconcerned about all this canonical reading sprouting from Mariátegui's programmatic agenda, maybe because it also had the inconvenience of showcasing his young talent more as a symptom of the crisis than as an active agent of change. Nonetheless, it is impossible to overlook the fact that as, for instance, the French Symbolists and the Italian Decadentists of the 19th Century had denounced the decline of their societies, Martín Adán was doing something similar in the context of the Peruvian Aristocratic Republic. With its scathing satire of Lima's icons, its ironic mistrust of Baroque traditions, its denunciation of political chicanery and its heartfelt complaint about the general feeling of anxiety and apathy, *The Cardboard House* was a decidedly spirited critique. Moreover, its rebelliousness often transcended its own representational content, displaying a penchant for grammatical transgression, polysemic wordplay, phonetical transformations and many other licenses that raised the narrative style of *The Cardboard House* to the level of some of the most innovative literary experimentalism of the times. All these qualities, rarely found together, had been consciously assumed by Mariátegui as the authentically revolutionary expressions of avant-garde art, and had constituted the core of *Amauta's* editorial line since its inception. With these considerations in mind, Mariátegui hastened to organize, like a modern-day John the Baptist, the coming of Martín Adán into the world. The first excerpt of *The Cardboard House* was published in 1927 in the 10th issue of *Amauta* (an excerpt that was ultimately eliminated from the final edition by the author). The book would appear the following year, with a foreword and a colophon by Luis Alberto Sánchez and José Carlos Mariátegui, respectively. In spite of their many differences and theoretical distances, we owe the recognition of *The Cardboard House* as a fundamental production of the times to Mariátegui's ecumenical spirit. He offered Martín Adán his sincere admiration, his friendship, and the complete logistic support for the publication of the novel, which was, in the words of Mariátegui himself, "a book whose success is fully assured".

Beyond Mariátegui's programmatic interpretation, which in a way pigeonholes *The Cardboard House* as a symptomatic production, dismissing the possibility of reading it as a political project, we must raise attention to Martín Adán's adamant skepticism regarding the political projects of modernity. Decades before the rise of Fascism and Sovietic terror, the young Adán already perceived the dangers of authoritarianism, alienation, and the binary simplification of the political spectrum that even the modern ideals of the avant-garde carried along their wake. Let us remember the fact that the two biggest populist ideologies of the era, Fascism and Communism, while being completely contrarian to each other, often found a common inspiration in the artistic crucible of avant-garde movements. From F.T. Marinetti's nationalist invectives to Andre Breton's anarchist utopias, it suffices to say that the ideologies of modernity and the avant-garde covered a wildly complex and contradictory spectrum. The point in question for Modernist utopias, specially in the fields of literature and the arts, had to do with a new conception of the human subject vis-a-vis the burgeoning technologies of Mass Culture and their relation to the State. The Nietzschean idea of the "Übermensch", for example, in spite of its ambiguity, became one of the flagship concepts for a generation of Promethean idealists and revolutionaries around the globe, who, by work and grace of erratic interpretations, felt justified to advance any sort of radicalism in its name. In contrast to this transcedentalist humanism, a common place for both the right and the left of the 1920's, Martín Adán strives to find in his subjective explorations a form of spiritual affirmation that actively refuses to be reduced to any preconceived idea of humanity. Quite the opposite, the explorations of *The Cardboard House* explicitly seek to find connections with animals and cosmic forces in an attempt to affirm potential "inhumanities". In this sense, Adán's Underwood Poems, the centerpiece of the book and a manifesto of sorts, turn out to be a lucid poetic disquisition against the political excesses of modernity; against all authoritarianism ("I don't want to be happy with the permission of the police") and against the idealism of Modernist utopias ("The world is overly ugly, and there is no way of embellishing it. I can only imagine it as a city of brothels and factories under a wing flap of red flags"). The question to ask is: Is it possible to find a political dimension in this poetic dissention, in this apparent apathy of the modern subject in regards to politics? We believe there is something more than just decadent pessimism in Martín Adán's asceticism, because there is so much more than just apathy in *The Cardboard*

House. There is also a good measure of adolescent humor, of creative irony, of healthy skepticism. And all these affirmative qualities are always aimed towards a discovery of sensations. For there is never a question of ideologies, but rather an experience of corporeal becoming, of raw sensations that are encountered anywhere and everywhere. We are dealing here with a coherent empiricism that, in its negation of the imperialism of ideologies, turns the body itself, with all its passions and affections, into the very field of politics. Martín Adán practices something we might call Militant Dilettantism: a will to proliferate corporal sensations in strict opposition to any sort of political program. With his denunciation of politics and his recreation of the body, he organizes an effective pragmatism that turns out to be of an exemplary Stoic sobriety when seen against the effervescent background of social struggles and collectivist utopias of the period. Like Fernando Pessoa, Franz Kafka or Roberto Arlt (some of the great "masters of suspicion" of the twentieth century), Martín Adán had perceived that there was something particularly questionable about all forms of Modernist Idealism, in its political slogans, in its programs and its revolutionary parties. Against the passionate heroism of most of his contemporaries, he affirms instead an *Epoché* —the suspension of judgment— as an ethical practice; and against the demands of political compromise, he discovers, in his poetic explorations, a series of very particular becomings: animal, molecular, geophysical and cosmic.

Therefore, more than being a satirical portrait of Lima and its picturesque peoples, as it has often been remarked, we would primarily describe *The Cardboard House* as a series of voyages-in-place: a collection of intensive explorations of desire and memory. These little creative exercises can begin from any point in space and time (a landscape, an image, a memory, an affect...) and from there start to draw, with the poetic movement of language, an excursion into places yet undiscovered in the world. Animals, children and inanimate objects become potential pivot points for the lines of flight of a budding desire trapped between the self and the others. The discoveries on these poetical explorations are never a trivial thing; for we are not simply dealing with idyllic, nostalgic or phantasmic images that pass in front of our eyes like in a projection screen. Rather it is the whole body that traverses these images, becoming itself affected by a transformation of the senses and perception. In these voyages, Martín Adán discovers many different ways of seeing and perceiving the world, and these are the fruitful productions of his new style and sensibility. That is why the scenes of *The Cardboard House* should be conceived more as freestyle exercises than as episodes in a linear narrative. No plot and no chapters, only motives and auspicious occasions for experimentation. The pragmatic program of *The Cardboard House* consists then in finding always a deeper dimension of the world by means of a decidedly precarious exercise in writing; an aleatory wandering in words, a purely experimental practice. Martín Adán, a 17 year old boy growing up in a grey and humid city in the confines of the tropics, enclosed within his four bedroom walls, opens up the picture windows of his notebook and his canine eyes transform into vectors that cut across boundaries, reaching into intimate microcosms in which everything becomes animated, in spaces where one can wander freely and finally flee, once again, towards the limiting planes of this old city-house: the earth, the sky and the sea. Sliding from the molecular to the cosmic, everything becomes a moldable material for this unbounded perception. Perhaps it can be objected that all these "becomings" are nothing more than fantasies, or products of the imagination, but one might ask in return if it is not precisely this productive imagination —a perceptual transformation of the senses— what is always needed throughout history, particularly for these so-called revolutionary movements. Which begs the question: what else could avant-garde art be about if it is not about transforming the world through art? *The Cardboard House* presents to us much more than a fragmented collection of images and offers us also an arsenal of techniques and methods with which to draw a diagram for the future.

So what is, concretely, the style of Martín Adán? What do we mean when we talk about his new techniques and methods? The significant influence of José María Eguren should be highlighted here, not only because Martín Adán, himself, recognizes Eguren's influence in the book dedication, but also because the effects of this influence in the book go far beyond the mere gestures of recognition and dedication. Eguren, remarkably, had liberated himself from many poetic conventions of the time, and in spite of being generally remembered as a foundational Symbolist poet, was also capable of overcoming the inherent limitations of any genre. By sometimes leaving aside the construction of metaphors and the prioritization of symbolic images, favoring instead phonetical resonances and a musical exploration of language, Eguren developed a poetic style that often dissociated itself from representational Symbolism in search of a playful, free lyricism with purely aesthetic considerations. In Eguren's poetry, the semiotic correspondences of images, their signifiers and signifieds, are usually combined with a free language game in which functions like resonance, suggestion, ambiguity and syntactical rearrangements come into play. Martín

Adán, directly following Eguren's pragmatics, dislocates his poetic expression from the strictly semiotic into a polyrhythmic language-game, effectively playing with words —with their sense and nonsense— in order to find creative and novel uses of language. However, we will insist on the point that there is always more that just a playful spirit of language in *The Cardboard House*. There is always a certain tension in the body, a double resistance to the closure of structures. Against political and aesthetical dogmatism, we find a total refusal to the repetition of formulas, to the consolidation of a unitary technique. Martín Adán lucidly organizes an adollescent rebellion against the oppresive agents of boredom; against their traditions, their morals and good manners. In this project he goes beyond a superficial critique of social formations, reaching also their deeper substrate, the established rules of expression and language conventions. In this insurrection against the rules of language we encounter: a rebellious use of syntax that joyfully disorders sentences; an aberrant use of punctuation, with the compulsive use of commas and dashes that create an effect of acceleration and breakage; the proliferation of free associations, puns and wordplay that, by dismantling the univocal relationship between signifiers and signifieds, open up multiple possibilities for interpretation. We will say that, in principle, the style of Martín Adán privileges the plastic dimension of language over the specific allocation of signifiance, and in this way *The Cardboard House* organizes nothing less than a total insurrection of linguistic signs. As for the images themselves, perhaps it would be a good approximation to say that, while Eguren resolved to turn into the past, to tradition and mythology, Martín Adán feels instead in constant agony, between fascination and anxiety, about the future. In response to the existential conundrums of modernity, Eguren had made his alliances with idyllic images of childhood, with the content of fables and magical animals; Martín Adán, on the other hand, finds his relays in the electric power of new technologies like the streetcar, the phonograph and the cinema screen. We find in *The Cardboard House* a style in constant transformation, always open to experimentation as a way of escaping into the future, directed by a constant will to keep reinventing himself and to slip away from the determinations of a single name, a single face, and a single voice. It has been said that Eguren was something of an eternal child; Martín Adán, on the other hand, cannot wait to grow up. Only he doesn't want to grow up to be an office clerk, a bussiness owner or even a succesful and respected writer. He doesn't know well what he wants to be, granted, but he knows very well what he will not ever be, that is, a repetition of the same oppresive past. Martín Adán has embarked in an adolescent project of liberation from the fate of centuries, from transcendence and predestination. To escape from these determinations, he denounces the visible agents of oppresion (the Church, the State...), but he also goes underground, to the connections of a language that overpowers him and subdues him, and at this level he tries to undo the networks of signifiance and replace them with a free association of signs. In this case, it is not a question of finding the right words to say what one means to say, but rather a question of letting the immanent possibilities of language proliferate in all directions, into transformations of every kind towards yet undiscovered possibilities. For words are like children: one has to let them play and talk freely among themselves in order to really hear what they have to say. In this playful combinatory tide of sense and nonsense, where the panoramic effect is an ambulatory movement of glossolalia and synesthesia, new potentials are always discovered. And language itself is transformed through this process, opening the range of potentials by a displacement of its function of univocal signification towards a polisemy of poetic expression. From a metaphysics of language —the determination of sense— to a pataphysics of language —the potentiality of nonsense—.

But, finally, all these theoretical considerations, which are nothing but our own attributions and interpretations, should not distract us too much from the fact that what ultimately determined the success of *The Cardboard House* was its outstandingly lucid and youthful spirit. There is a lot of romantic instinct in Martín Adán, of a concrete idealism that doesn't have anything to do with ideologies, but rather, with ideals. If we had to define *The Cardboard House* in a single sentence, we would say that, above all, it is an extended poem dedicated to the creative youth of all times; a love letter to his generation, and specially to the milieu of Barranco, preferential land of musicians and poets. Nobody has quite recreated the bohemian allure of Barranco like Martín Adán; its colorful streets, its easygoing spirit, its mysterious nights with mellow skies and cool breeze at the edge of the sea. Martín Adán speaks to us sincerely about that time in our lives when the world seems to be too big and yet irresistible, when we want to run away and fall in love and discover the night, with all its mysteries and dangers. Much like Joyce's *Portrait of the Artist as a Young Man* (that, as Luis Alberto Sánchez tells us, Adán had attempted to translate when he was still a high school student), *The Cardboard House* is both a period piece and a coming-of-age novel that immediately resonated with its readers, a generation growing amidst the contradictory forces of tradition and revolution, in a real turn of the century that felt both like a historical challenge and an unsurmountable force. As Mariátegui predicted, *The Cardboard House* was destined to become an immediate success and an influential book for the years to come. For the Latin American Boom generation of the 1960's-70's, for instance, the rediscovery of *The Cardboard House* decades after its publication represented an early paradigm of literary innovation, and has been regarded since then as a major statement in Latin American literature, receiving generous commentaries by important authors such as Mario Vargas Llosa, and more recently, César Aira and Roberto Bolaño. Unfortunately, Martín Adán would spend the rest of his life in a progressive deterioration, battling alcoholism and mental illness, coming in and out of mental institutions. He never wrote anything like *The Cardboard House* again, turning its production instead into a profoundly hermetic and metaphysical poetic work that has also been unanimously celebrated. In any case, his prestige as a writer only grew in time, together with the stories about his disordered life and his fame of *poète maudit*. But this is the stuff of legends that here we can only mention in passing. To reminisce him we will evoke the American beat poet Allen Ginsberg[4], who briefly met Adán while traveling in Perú

4. *Ginsberg, Allen. "To An Old Poet In Perú" in Reality Sandwiches. City Lights. San Francisco. 1963.* About Ginsberg's encounter with Martín Adán see: *Casusol, Pedro. Divine Visions: Allen Ginsberg's Peruvian trip*. https://ebsn.eu/scholarship/articles/visiones-divinas-divine-visions-allen-ginsbergs-peruvian-trip/

in the 1960's and, intrigued by his personality, decided to dedicate him a few poems. In one of these verses we read: "your obscure shuffle is the motion of a seraphim that has lost its wings". An accurate portrait of Martín Adán, this fallen angel who even at 17 years of age was already like one of his cardboard characters, a little too wild and a little too mischievous, even while being completely serious. A dreamer in his own terms who, in his older days, still stumbled outside the bars to go on a nocturnal stroll, as he had done so for decades, along the streets and to the seafronts, wandering around the city at night in search of his young rebel soul.

José Garay Boszeta

A note on the new translation

There are always numerous reasons to embark in a new translation of a previously published work. The essential prerequisite remains, perhaps, in the personal relationship that the aspiring translator has with the work in question. *The Cardboard House* is a book that has constantly inspired us across the years, and to which we have returned frequently in order to better find ourselves and our own affections. This new translation has, as its only motivation, the purpose of becoming a retribution to the legacy and memory of Martín Adán. Since a translation should always be primarily a tribute to the author, we feel that the eventual translator can only aspire to be a neutral medium for the author's voice. The many complexities of literary translation undoubtly open up a crucial space of critical interpretation for the translator. And if translation is an art, as it has been often remarked, we believe there is one rather chimerical challenge for a translator's interpretation: the art of rendering itself, in turn, imperceptible.

This new translation of *The Cardboard House* started after reading the English translation by Katherine Silver (Graywolf Press, 1990; New Directions, 2012). Even though Mrs. Silver's translation has many remarkable aspects, we are of the opinion that it doesn't ultimately succeed in transmitting the spirit of the novel from its original Spanish language into English. The problems for translation arise from the fact that *The Cardboard House* is an experimental avant-garde text with a notoriously peculiar relationship with language. In this sense, any successful translation of *The Cardboard House* must, in our opinion, convey to the reader an approximate, analogous feeling of displacement in relation to language. The shortcomings of Mrs. Silver's translation are mainly due to her decision of constantly rearranging Adán's idiosincratic syntax into a standarized English form. The result is that Adán's intentional resolve for the atypical phrase in the original is often lost in translation. Even thought it's entirely true that Spanish generally presents a more flexible syntax than English, and therefore, it's sometimes neccesary to rearrange the phrases in translation in order to make sense, we believe nonetheless that this particular dimension of *The Cardboard House*, namely, Adán's penchant for the novel configuration of words, is completely missing in Mrs. Silver's translation. The same goes for Adán's aberrant use of punctuation, which he constanty uses as a technique for creating intensive markers in the text. In lieu of this, we find either a resetting of punctuation into a standarized model, or a reorganization of punctuation in ways that are not at all present in the original. Finally, there is a series of misinterpretations that range from the trivial to the severe, as well as unexpected additions and, what is worse, inexplicable omissions of certain key terms that are crucial for understanding Adán's wordplay in the original. All of these drawbacks have as their consequence a regrettable flattening of Adán's rebellious style into the normative rules of English grammar.

Due to its uncanny plasticity in relation to language, *The Cardboard House* poses challenges for the translator that usually exceed the common situations encountered in literary translation, opening up in turn spaces for delicate interpretations. This new translation has carefully attempted to reproduce the style and vocabulary of *The Cardboard House* into an analogous English form. The reader must bear in mind that what appears to be grammatical errors in the following text (even though we don't claim to be completely exempt of them) are, for the most part, conscious decisions stemming from our own translation criteria. It would be beside the point here to indicate in detail the particulars of every situation and the differences in relation to previous translations. We have done our best to indicate, by means of footnotes along the text, what these challenges have been for us, as well as our own solutions. We have also made use of footnotes in order to clarify some of the references that specifically relate to the Peruvian context of the 1920's. In any case, and in spite of these neccesary remarks, the present translation is decidely indebted to Mrs. Silver translation, and it has been carefully compared with it in order to reach its own conclusions.

The present volume also includes the foreword by Luis Alberto Sánchez and the colophon by José Carlos Mariátegui. These two sections, which constituted an integral component of *The Cardboard House* since its first publication in 1928, had not been included in Mrs. Silver's editions. We have decided to include them because they represent important historic documents for understanding Martín Adán's relationship with the literary Avant-garde of the time; they remain, to this day, as some of the best commentaries to *The Cardboard House.*

Exhibition at Casa Columbia. Lima, 1931. Left to right: Martín Adán, Alida Elguera, José Torres de Vidaurre and José María Eguren.

THE CARDBOARD HOUSE
— 1928 —

Foreword

To Martín Adán

If it wasn't for you, I would have never accepted to repeat my luck. With this one it's two times I'm bullfighting in conjunction with Mariátegui, and, truth be told, the public is going to shriek from the covert. The previous one I got the colophon and he the foreword, for Tempest in the Andes. Now he has gotten the colophon and I, the foreword. "Not for my money —the connoisseurs are shouting—: this is a repetition of the same"; and, by the way, it's better to avoid certain comparisons...

But I cannot deny you some lines on the porch of this

book, which is a battle won. Rafael de la Fuente Benavides, my ex-disciple when I was "Herr Lehrer in der Deutschen Schule", and he, a very exemplary student, dictates here his testament. And I come to serve him as a witness, as a candleholder in this extreme unction for an aristocratic, clerical and civilist[5] man. Gynecology will know the secret of how Martín Adán appeared.

But, Martín Adán, while being different from Rafael de la Fuente Benavides, has in similarity to him, the demure and his modest gesture. From Proust he learned perhaps a certain parsimonious delectation in describing, and from Joyce, the tattletale accent of a sexton. De la Fuente should have been a friar. It seems to me that sometime I heard saying, when he was a child, that he felt the ecclesiastical vocation. Fortunately, the irony, the readings, and the cigarettes, somewhat roughed up his piping voice and pasty vocation. We will never properly appreciate the influence of cigarettes in literature. Therefrom have emerged those coffeehouse poets, those charlatans of brothel gossipmongery, those evocators who pause the story with long puffs like the chimney smoke from a "steamer." But, not even cigarettes have been able to entirely erase the catholic

---

5. Sociopolitical movement centered around the Peruvian Civilista Party. The politics of *Civilismo* signaled the development of Capitalism and the modern State in Peruvian society during the 19th and 20th century.

and modest attitude of Martín Adán. He is still an aristocrat, a half clerical, a bloke from Joyce, kind of a "Stephen Dedalus", even if he does avant-garde art.

Because, without a doubt, this is the avant-garde art. To some it seems it's not and, of course, within a political monochordia, everything that does not transcribe a social zeal, turns out apolitical and backwards. If he were so, Adán would coincide with their tendency, with their literary *Chouannerie*[6] at bottom, even though the form is jumping with novelties. Novelties superior to those of almost all of these gentlemen who pretend to manage the current prose among us, and turn out to be some very sad apes, who steal metaphors and tales from Beingolea (previously translated into Spanish). At least De la Fuente has saved his epidermis from this terrible intellectual meridian of the Americas, translation —as said by some rightful malevolent from *Gaceta*[7] — and has opened his spirit to winds that are not of Spanish exclusivity, as in the times of the galleons.

De la Fuente is the avant-garde, due to his freshness of images, to his dislocation, to his humorism, to his

---

6. *i.e. Servilism.* Jean Chouan (1757-1794) was a royalist partisan who commanded a popular insurrection for the restoration of the Monarchy during the French Revolution. The episode was fictionalized by Barbey D'Aurevilly in his novel, Le Chevalier des Touches (1964).

7. *Gaceta de Lima.* Peruvian conservative newspaper founded in 1743.

sportsmanship in the style; yet this zeal for crafting literature and phrases, accuses a certain decadentism distant from the Rubenian rhythm, but, it is not, because of that, less decadent. What is decadent is always aristocratic, but there is an avant-garde of the decadent, and this is the one Martín Adán practices. With this he ratifies that the civilist within him has not died. We are simply attending to his extreme unction. The "requiescat" trembles on the lips, but it is not so easy to break free from the pressure, yet unimbibed, of the leagues with an "Index expurgatorum" for the remiss volitions and guardian angels who are entertained with a music of pianola. Yet Martín Adán, who has turned by the deed of the first pages of this book, into literature, is in danger of falling into the arms of the «Entre Nous», and that his delicacy could convince the sighful young ladies of that center of selection, declamation and temper. He is backed solely, by the relative critical acuteness of such virtuous ladies for whom the cycle of Ruben is just beggining, the accursed one of yesteryear and so full of aristocracies today, with his sad princess, his Ledas and his swans, now so discredited that they have even disappeared from our Zoological Park.

In addition, Martín Adán has a very fatal pruritus for being disciplined. At least, that's how Rafael de la Fuente was, in the "Deutsche Schule." Had he been born in another time, he would have been a supporter of García Moreno, and he is the owner of an excellent temper for a soldier. That is why one must distrust the juggling and contortions of his literature. A lot of vigilant volition has trained that style. And Martín Adán, who is a great literary masseuse, has thinned out his ways, has forced them to acrobatics, taught them the somersault, the triple mortal jump, the fall of the angel and the walk of death, by force of care, of a firm decision to be dislocated. Gypsy of his verb, he kidnapped it when it barely babbled, and has succeded in breaking its joints in order to force it to all kinds of pirouettes. He displays, therefore, a nonchalance that the public men who march to Europe with the illusion of Voronoff[8] would certainly wish for themselves...

The Cardboard House opens its fragile doors to the reader's curiosity. An alert good taste, some tireless pruningshears, and an authentic artistic sense have raised these walls with toys, wherein Ramón has his adolescent ravings. Perfectly adolescent. Sex peeps out, urgent but inexperienced, and there is delight, concealed among verbal exquisiteness, when Catita emerges, or even if it is the fat aunt, with the bobble stitch robe. Ramón

[8] *i.e. with great expectations.* Serge Voronoff (1866-1951) was a French surgeon who gained fame during the 1920's for his techniques of male rejuvenation, which were often disparaged as quackery.

is at the age when every woman seems angelic. But, then, because of that, *The Cardboard House* is going to become the Madmen House, for many national critics. Martín Adán does wrong in giving them, all of a sudden, a prose that is going to rabble-rouse the little sense that still remained forgotten inside their skulls.

We shall talk about Eguren, once the book appears. Indeed, Eguren, to whom the book is dedicated, was the tutelary act of Martín's childhood. He taught him the love for the sullen and modest word; the disaffection for the hard and plebeian term; the fervor of a Renaissance imaginer for his prose; a patent of patient artist, tenacious, very delicate. But Martín emancipated himself from Eguren, because it is not easy for anyone to remain in that unique world of José María. Reality is not so easily isolated like that, by the poets. And Eguren is in the literature of the Americas a unique and formidable case of an effectively suprarealist imaginer, a creator of a cosmos, a begetter of figures with a technique and a teleology definitively personal. Vallejo, the other great poet of ours, enters into literature under the sign of Herrera Reissig, but life overcomes him. There is authentic blood in his poems, as there is celestial dream in Eguren, as there is life, but without pain yet, only twitches, still without agony, in Martín Adán. This emancipated teenager is in need of living. He has not left the «Stephen Dedalus» school. And nevertheless, *The Cardboard house* will scandalize the right-wing and will be a toy for children, a tantrum for older people.

The readers should not let themselves be scammed. I have erected myself as their policeman, so that they won't be credulous about many of Martín's attitudes, the first one: do not have faith in his discombobulation. He was —I know this— an advantaged and disciplined student of Spanish, and he perfectly knew the rules of agreement, the method of diformisms, the semantic reason in spelling. Furthermore, he very much loves his prose, his style, as to forsake it. Let's remember that thing about being the masseuse and the gypsy of his verb, and with that I intend to gain an enthusiastic adhesion. This newly-appeared writer has a strange way of coming to the fore. He appears in a trio, but in a bellicose trio. Since he has the knack for it and the personality, he endures the bashing. We are not dealing with a good-fornothing who is afraid of disputes. Although Eguren had taught him to be modest, he, previously, had enjoyed a certain coprolalia in his writings. The cigarette, the coprolalia: accomplices in the loss of his clerical vocation. Now, it will be difficult for him to straighten the path. Someone has said that the world turns to the left, and Martín slides to the left. There is nothing to be done. But, to be sure, he understands the literary left, totally apolitical.

Totally artistic, totally literary. And if humanity cannot live without politics, and if even this work is explained by a political reason, I'm sure then that *The Cardboard House* was raised by Martín in a limbo, in the clouds, anywhere, where he could only be reached by the rumor of his literary avocations and where he could craft for himself the illusion of being clerical and civilist. Only that Civilism is no longer a political party, but a way of being, a term that instead of being in Burguess, in Schmoller, in our friend Távara, (El Comercio, year 62) should be listed in Freud or in Doctor Delgado.[9]

My dear Martín: reject that thing about your filiation to Anatole France; you are not a necrophage. And France, already, to our artistic criteria full of vitalism, has been exposed as "a corpse." Because even in Eguren one finds the passion and the restlessness. And you, who read very little of Antonio Azorín, but who before the Spanish edition of *A Portrait of the Artist as a Young Man* assayed a translation of Stephen Dedalus, know very well that

---

9. — Gustav von Schmoller (1838-1917). German economist. Leader of the Historical school of economics.
— Federico Mould Távara (1907-1958). Peruvian writer and diplomat.
— El Comercio, is a Peruvian newspaper based in Lima. Founded in 1839, it is the oldest newspaper in Perú and one of the most influential publications in the country.
— Honorio Delgado (1892-1969). Peruvian psychiatrist. One of the first disciples of Freud in Perú.

it is not skepticism what inspires your vision of things, but rather a concern for finding what is certain, and the hesitation to be treading in the void. Agony, but silent and pudorous. The twilight of a soft maiden from the book of saints.

Luis Alberto Sánchez

Portrait of Martín Adán captured by José María Eguren with his mini photographic camera. 18 x 30 mm. Lima, circa 1930.

To José María Eguren

The winter has already begun in Barranco; weird winter, ditzy and fragile, that seems like it is going to plunge into the sky and let a tip of summer peek out. Little fog of the tiny winter, thing of the soul, puffs of the sea, drizzles of a boat trip from one pier to another, sonorous flapping of retarded lay sisters, opaque mumble of Masses, winter just arrived... Now one has to go to school with cold in the hands. The breakfast is a hot ball in the stomach, and a hardness of dining room chair in the buttocks, and a solemn desire of not going to school in the whole body. A palm tree sticks out above a house with the frond, flabelliform, softly somber, whole, rosy, fulgid. And now you whistle in the streetcar, boy with eyes closed. You don't comprehend how is it possible to go to school so early in the morning and having seafronts with sea below. But, as you pass by the long street that is almost all of the city, you smell the juicing of remote legumes in nearby orchards. You think of the full and wet countryside, almost urban if one looks back, but that has no limits if one looks ahead, in between the alders and the ash trees, to the bluish sierra. Barely the limits of the firstly foothills, eyebrows of mountain... And now you go through the countryside in a deaf bee like murmur of quickly rubbed railtracks and in a gymnastic of athletic although urban airs. Now the sun chews sallow a mountain peak and a *huaca*[10], a hillock yellow as the very sun. And you do not want it to be summer, but instead winter of vacations, very tiny and weak, with no school and no heat.

Beyond the countryside, the sierra. Beneath the countryside, a brook bordered with alders and with women who wash rags and rascals, one another the same color of indifferent dirt. It is two in the afternoon. The sun strives to free its beams from the trap of branches into which it has fallen. The sun —a coleopteran, rare, hard, sallow, leggy—. Mister parish priest pulls from

10. A huaca or wak'a is an object that represents something revered, typically a pre-Columbian archeological monument of some kind.

his shovel hat, tilting the head, eleven reflections of a tall silk hat, of a ceremonial jar —the eleven reflections come together above, in a convex round light—. Beyond the city, the clear and tender chasm of the sea. The sea is seen from above, in danger of falling down the slope. The cliffs have wrinkles and unpolluted smoothnesses, and lividities and yellow spots of a geological, academic forehead. There they are, in miniature, the four epochs of the world, the four dimensions of things, the four cardinal points, everything, everything. One old man... two old men... three old men... three *Pierolistas*[11]. Three hours of sunlight must be wrested from the night. The clothes turn out to be large in excess to the body. The overbrushed cloth, it corners, it treaks[12], it falls, it tenses —the cloth, hollow inside—. The bones creak to the beat in the beating actioning, in the rhythmic reaching of the hands to the sky in the horizon —plane surface that cuts that of the sea, forming an angle X, last chapter of the elementary geometry (first course)—; the heaven where Piérola must be. The moustaches of the old men cut finely, into slices like expensive marmalade, a sea

[11.] Supporters of Nicolas de Piérola (1839-1913), Peruvian politician who served as President during the reconstruction years that followed the War of the Pacific.

[12.] That breaks in three directions. Triedra, in the original, is a portmanteau of tres (three) and quiebra (breaks).

breeze and impregnate it with the odor of ragwort, of tobacco from Tumbes, of herbal handkerchief, of *criollo*[13] cough syrups. A flag of six colors, while billowing slowly by a very high wind, insensible below, delates flanks of a Spanish dancer. General Consulate of Tomesia, country that Giraudoux made with a Hungarian plain, two millionaires from Lima, some English trees and a sky tone of Chinese embroidery. Tomesia, not far from its General Consulate anywhere. An ice cream vendor's cart goes past an old nag horse that dangles out the rough and whitish big tongue. The poor animal would eat with delight the ice creams of the hidden cube —*lucuma*[14] essence ice cream, opaque and elegant flavor, barely cold; milk ice cream, ample and pretty like a youthful portrait of mom at the side of dad; pineapple essence ice cream that corresponds to the red carnations; orange essence ice cream, mild and not known at all—. How does the cart sound! With the rocks it goes breaking up its soul the poor thing. And not for anything in the world amends its path —the straight path right through the walls on the dead-end

---

[13]. The Criollos were a social class in the caste system of the Latin American colonies established by Spain in the 16th century. The name was used for people of pure or mostly Spanish blood, but who were born in the colony. By extension, it refers to the picaresque people and customs of Lima.

[14]. The fruit of the Lucuma tree is almost exclusively used to make ice cream.

streets, straight to imbecility—. Little cart, come along this grass, that the water of the fountain keeps soft for you. There are among things, leagues of mutual aid, that man impedes. The sounding of the cart's wheels in the pavement rocks cheers up the fountain from the sad waters in the pool. The *cholo*[15], with cheeks of blood-soaked dirt and the nose sprinkled with sweat in atomic, round drops, the cart driving *cholo* does not let the cart go over the grass of the wispiest garden. The old men observe: —"It is cold. Yesterday?... Beautiful day! So tell us, Mr. So-and-so..."

In the morning, at the edge of the dawn, from the fenestras in the towers, in a clumsy flight of frightened birds and wet bell strokes, the old lay sisters go down to the coven of the trees and the light poles in the mist. Blacknesses that move from here to there, infinite arms, hooky hands, half-heard precepts... And the city is an oleography submerged in water that we contemplate: the wavelenghts carry the things away and alter the disposition of the plane surfaces. Lay sisters who smell

[15]. Native South American indian. Cholo is a term charged with social and racial overtones, but its colloquial use is highly dependent on context and it can range from the derogatory to a term of endearment.

of sun and morning dew, of the humidity of towels forgotten behind the bath tub, of elixirs, of eye drops, of the devil, of sponges, of that hollow and dry smell of used limestone, tinctured, soaped... Lay sisters who smell of dirty clothes, of stars, of cat skin, of lamp oil, of whale sperm... Lay sisters who smell of tumbleweed, of darkness, of the litany, of flowers for the dead... Straight coats, metallic slippers... The rosary goes in the heart and it is not heard.[16] At twelve in the morning, the sun falls down, liquid and leaden as a yellow gouache from an ancient carnival. The streetcars passing their shipload of hats. Oh, the wind, what a joy in this sea of seriousness. All the *"Cronicas"* and *"Comercios"*[17] are billowing!, so much that one fears a reverse gear of the car, almost a slanted flight over the rails and the light poles. A tollbooth gets to safety with a jump. The factory stops the car like a ball that rolls in the classroom, as the teacher does.

---

[16]. *el rosario va en el seno y no suena.* We have attempted to substitute the wordplay between seno/suena (breast/sound) for heart/heard.

[17]. Two of the most popular Peruvian newspapers of the era.

The afternoon, for the last time. Now we are passing by the Saint Francis square, under a broken chiming of *novena.*[18] A wall that doesn't allow to see the towers —cutely ugly— shows, instead, illuminated by fronting glimpses of sky, three picture windows, of blue sleepy crystals. Down this street one goes to the sea —like in the great seaports, to a sea that is not seen—. It is not today when we passed by the Saint Francis square; it was yesterday when we did, insofar as you were telling me that the twilight was hurting your eyes. You were chewing a little shrub leaf and rubbing the nails on one of your hands with the ones on the other. I was afraid of your confidences —always overly sincere—; to keep you from speaking, I remembered, out loud, one remote afternoon that, as in the wisecrack, was a great fried egg —a sun of brilliant gold and in relief, almost in the periphery of a watery and uneven porcelain sky— a nutritive afternoon that stained with dusk the face up to the nose of the gluttonous poets. The cinemas moo in their dark and filthy mangers. A buzzard, on the tip of a flagstaff, is a poult —curved blackness and grey beak—. An old woman wandered by the seafront aimlessly, and

[18]. A traditional Catholic prayer that is repeated for nine consecutive days.

then, dramatic, went away by I don't know where. An automobile turned on a headlight, which revealed a cone of drizzle. We felt cold in the eyelids. Yesterday... Bass Street now comforts with bedroom shadows, with drugstorey odors of eucalyptus, with medical words, with its promenades of paludic trees. And there is nobody who is not you or me.

Ramón put the glasses on and ended up looking curlier than ever in the face and legs. He said yes and filled up his pockets with the hands. A bright star trembled in the sky; another bright star trembled closer by. The sky was blue with nighttime, with loose threads of daytime, with threads of the day, feminine, seamstressy. The scissors of the wind were sounding as in a barbershop and one didn't know if it was one's own hair they were cutting or the chinese silk of the sky. Humbly, Ramón divested himself of his hope as if he had divested himself of his hat. —Life, and him that was starting to live... One must resign oneself, he quoted Schopenhauer and puffed profoundly, as if sleeping—. I preferred Kempis to Schopenhauer. Nietzsche was a phony. Ramón had not read Nietzsche, but he had indeed heard talking about the Superman. He knew that Superman was an alias of Firpo. Was starting to live... The compulsory military service... A possible war... The children, inevitable... Old age... The work of every day.... I delicately whispered him consolations, but I couldn't console him; he hunched the back and knit the brow; his elbows asserted themselves on his knees; he was a failure. At sixteen years old!... Oh, what had befallen him! He almost cried; a spinster in a bicycle prevented it. A bright star crackled in the sky; another bright star faded out closer by. A mongrel and passerby dog, was looking at us walking, looking back. I made characters for him with the fingers: —"It isn't anything. Don't you be inconvenient"—. We went to Lima. In the sticky asphalt, automobile tires were sizzling; at the end of every street, a sundown of golden satin; the telephone poles were backlighting themselves perfectly; the street urchins were still proclaiming the morning. We returned to Barranco at night.

This one was an Englishman who fished with a rod. On a long face of terracotta, the nose thick and tall; below, the mouth of friar, immobile and sunk, with the lips within; and a purest Catacaos hat[19]; and a shaved hand; and a long, long, long rod... Without a doubt, this Englishman was as every fisherman, an idiot, but he didn't balance the legs, rather yet, he affirmed the feet in the support rail, slippery as a floor tile out of sheer mossiness... What was this Englishman fishing, careless lampfish or miniscule blennies? I think he wasn't fishing anything but a seaweed from hour to hour with a drop at the ending that swelled and plummeted before he would catch it. A poet?... Nothing of the sort: a traveling agent of the Dawson & Brothers house, but he fished with a rod. And the temptation of pushing him, and the Catacaos floating, and the rod nailed like a mast in the sand at the bottom...

In the bewitched mirror of the rainy street: drop of milk, the opaline globe of a lamppost; drop of water, the sky above; drop of blood, one's own self through this stupid joy of winter that arrives without warning... I am now the man without race and without age who appears in the geography treatises, with the ridiculous

[19]. Traditional hand-woven straw hats from the north of Perú, known for their high quality.

clothes, with the shadowy face, with the open arms, orienting herbs of Chinese ink and carbonated clouds —the scraggy, broken landscape of the engraving—: over here the West; the North, on this wall; the South to my back. Over this way one goes to Asia. Over this way, to Africa. Everything that is beyond the sierra or the sea comes close suddenly, meridian to meridian, in one man, above the ebony waters of the sidewalk. The Turk is the Levant and the Occident, tightened bundle of latitudes: the face, Spanish; the pants, French; the nose, Roman; the eyes, German; the tie, Bulgarian; the rucksack, Russian; the restlessness, Jewish... If we go through the East, the enumeration increases. If through the West, it decreases. Dakar or Peking. Haremic joy of the blue fabric when peeking through the holes, of the dun borders of the black rubber. The countryside, rashed with *huacas*[20], in the open mouth of the streets. Penumbra of drizzle that falls. Trees with the birds wet. It is for a reason that the world is round... And these cars, dirty with haste, with pride, with mud... The fig trees make the houses grow in their mirages of folliage of mud and moss, almost water, almost water, water above and below, the sediments, chlorophyll or clay,

[20] Cf. note 10, p. 52.

what do I know... Sparrows, grasshoppers. One's own self opens the eyes round, ichthyologized. In the water, inside the water, the lines break, and the surface has the images at its mercy. No, at mercy of the force that moves it. But it is the same, in the end and after all. Pavement of asphalt, fine and fragile sheet of mica... A narrowest street thickens, in order that two vehicles —a cart and another cart— when coupling, can continue together, the one next to the other. And everything is thus trembling, obscure, like on a cinema screen.

A minuscule and barren jacaranda never seemed to Ramón like an Englishwoman with eyeglasses. In vain strolled around Barranco day and night a half crazy gringa, photophobic, photographer, delight of a boarding house of clean drapes and cretonne curtains. The gringa was an ambulatory road, blind with sun, by which one went to the tundras, to a country of snow and moss where stood up a lean and livid city of skyscrapers with all the mistery of mechanics in the shadowy factories. The life of Miss Annie Doll had to be remounted in sleigh and in airplane, in automobile and in transatlantic. And at the end of her, Miss Annie

Doll was a reddish child breastfed with a sanitary bottle. Synthetic milk, canned meat, solid alcohol, seven years of sports academy, reindeers and squirrells, trips to China, collections of archaeology in a Manchester suitcase in which the whole civilization fits, tablets of aspirin, odor of sawdust of the hotel dining rooms, odor of smoke in the high seas, on board... In so many things you make one think, photophobic gringa, photographer gringa, who lives in a boarding house that is a humongous building with its third floor of grey planks, with its sorrows of railroad station and of henhouse! Gringa, road of sun glare that leads to the tundra, to Vladivostock, to Montreal, to the North Pole, to white scientific schools of perpetual winter, to anywhere...

But Ramón does not see in the jacaranda your image dilated by the sun. You, for him you are a half-crazy gringa, and a jacaranda, a tree that casts purple flowers. You are a long, sinewy, red, very mobile thing, that carries a Kodak on the side and asks questions of wisdom, of uselessness, of foolishness... A jacaranda is a solemn, antiquated, confidential, expressive, gaudy, reminiscer, uncle tree. You, almost a woman; a jacaranda, almost a man. You, human, in spite of everything; him, tree, if we leave off the poetry.

Ramón, I do not think about the splendid jacarandas

in the Park. Miss Annie Doll nothing has to see in them except her antithesis —a vegetal antithesis, full of nature and supreme truth—. But there is a jacaranda on a hidden street that smells of bananas —a street of laundries, zigzagging; an alley of whitewashed walls, without doors or windows that give a certain light of military hospital or school premises just inaugurated—. And the jacaranda that is on that street is the one I say is the gringa, I don't know if a jacaranda that is the gringa or if the gringa that is a jacaranda. Is the tree I don't know if too young or too old. Before it we hesitate as before the huacos[21] of the Museum, which we don't know if they're from Nazca or from Chimu, if authentic or forged, if black or white. Perhaps the jacaranda of Mott street is young or old at the same time, like the gringa, —lanky, almost butt-naked altogether, with a single foliated arm, with a stump of raped flowers, free, that seems to have been thrown into the wind—. Ramón, remember. We have gone afternoons and afternoons, you and me, to Mott Street to hear the bell strokes of the vespertine angelus —rainbow-colored soap bubbles that the puerile Saint Francis launches from the blowpipes

[21]. In this context, *huacos* refers to pieces of pre-Columbian ceramic found in archeological sites.

of the towers of his church in a heaven for a child—. Ramón, don't you remember how the bell strokes then bursted above; how there was neither vision nor sound of them, but only a cold odor of water, all too brief and mild for us to be able to notice it at the moment in which it was wetting our faces, turned towards the sundown? The sundown was a withered banana behind the Elysian bananas of Mott Street. But let's forget the jacaranda and the bells of Saint Francis. Let's remember Miss Annie Doll, tourist and photographer, coil spring dressed with jersey that jumped out of the box of surprises of the Peruvian resort. One pressed a button, and Miss Annie Doll hurled away the body and the yellow eyeglasses. The toy was a municipal attraction, it could not be bought, it was everybody's, absolutely public. The city and Miss Annie Doll... She lived of a rent that came from far away, fabulously from far away, like a can of tea; she spoke a Latin that shattered her teeth of clean crockery like a crystal, into a thousand smithereens; she did not comprehend the bell strokes of Saint Francis, because she happened to hear them in Hebrew, and Saint Francis did not know dead languages, but only how to make soap bubbles to cheer up God; she used some eyeglasses with the same tortoiseshell frame as yours, but the lenses in hers were yellow, antiluminiscent. And you, Ramón, are not a neurasthenic boy nor do you suffer from any sort of conjunctivitis. Ramón, normal boy... But the gringa looks, like it or not, essentially like... what do I know... the jacaranda of Mott Street.

On the streetcar. Seven-thirty in the morning. A glimpse of sun under the low short drapes. Tobacco smoke. An erect old lady. Two poorly shaved priests. Two salesclerks. Four female typists, with their laps full of notebooks. One schoolboy —me—. Another schoolboy —Ramón—. Smells like bed and cresol. The color of sun settles on the windows' crystals by the outer side like a cloud of pale translucid butterflies. Sudden excess of passengers. A sinister old woman, with the skin of crepe paper, of the same crepe of her cloak, on the seat that Ramón was occupying. Ramón, hanging from a door —that of the motorist— turning the head and the eyes in opposite directions. On Ramón's eyeglasses there is a meek fulgor of philosophy. Ramón carries the last afternoon —that of yesterday— in the wallet. He goes to school, because he's late, and he is late because he goes to school. I go with him, close to him, with obscure dislike of my feet not reaching the ground. But, conversely, in my overly long hand, fit the spines of all my textbooks. And that is a pleasure, almost a consolation, for my pedantic fourteen years. My life hangs from a first grade like a little bread crumb from a thread of spider web. Ramón, suddenly, extends to me above a bald head, a stamp in which there is an angel with a face of constipation and a villainous twilight in the first place. A gift from Catita eenie, meenie, miney, mo, boarding school silliness, frolicking of nuns and the long jump rope that makes afternoon ellipses. Catita, date of a desert palm tree... But to the lord are pleasant only the dates of the palm trees that "Mamére" prunes; the dates for which is thankful in a little basket with a perfect tie of white silk on the handle —untruthful butterfly— the implausible mister chaplain. Innocent dates, dates from Palestine.... The slums of Lima. An oil factory swells its sticky belly and puffs like a drunk old woman— Lima. The police, in the morning of a deep blue, bounces from uniform to uniform a whistle still in diapers, that shrieks and covers its eyes with the fists. And, suddenly, the shadow of the school slips inside my eyes like the night.

My first love was age twelve and had the black nails. My then Russian soul, in that little town of eleven thousand souls and a publicist priest, fostered the loneliness of the ugliest girl with a grievous, social, somber love, that was like the penumbra in a session of an international workers' congress. My love was vast, dark, slow, with beards, spectacles and handbags, with sudden incidents, with twelve languages, with stalking from the police, with troubles from many sides. She used to tell me, while getting into sex: you are a socialist. And her little soul of a learner of European nuns would open like an intimate prayer book by the part that deals with the deadly sins.

My first love was going away from me, frightened of my socialism and my foolishness. "Lest all of them are socialists..." And she promised herself to give herself to the first old Christian who passed by, even if this one had not reached the twelve years of age. Alone already, I moved away from the utmost problems and fell truly in love with my first love. I felt an agonic need, toxicomaniac, of inhaling, until bursting my own lungs, the smell of her; smell of little schoolhouse, of Chinese ink, of enclosure, of sun on the patio, of state-issued paper, of aniline, of cotton mesh worn barely under the skin —smell of the Chinese ink, thin and black—, almost a tracing pen of ebony, ghost on vacation... And this was my first love.

My second love was fifteen years of age. A crybaby with a lost set of teeth, with braids of hemp, with freckles all over the body, without family, without ideas, overly futuristic, excessively feminine... I was rival to a doll of rag and celluloid that wouldn't do anything but laugh at me with a rascally and stupid bigmouth. I had to understand an endless amount of perfectly unintelligible things. I had to say an endless amount of perfectly unspeakable things. I had to do well on the exams, with one hundred —suspicious grade, embarrassing, ridiculous: a hen in front of an egg—. I had to see her pamper her dolls. I had to hear her cry for me. I had to suck hard candies of all the colors and flavors. My second love abandoned me as in a tango: a malefactor...

My third love had the cute eyes, and the legs very coquettish, almost *cocottes*[22]. Fray Luis de León and Carolina Invernizzio had to be read. Peregrine girl... I don't know why she fell in love with me. I consoled myself of her irrevocable decision to be a friend of mine after having been almost my lover, with the twelve orthographic mistakes of her last letter.

---

[22] *coquetas, casi cocotas.* From the French *cocotte*, a fashionable prostitute.

My fourth love was Catita.

My fifth love was a dirty girl with whom I sinned almost in the night, almost in the sea. The remembrance of her smells like she smelled, like the shadow of a cinema, like a wet dog, like underwear, like confectionery, like warm bread, superimposed smells and, in and of themselves, individually, almost unpleasant, like the layers of cakes, ginger, meringue, etcetera. The sum of odors made of her a true temptation for a seminarian. Dirty, dirty, dirty... My first deadly sin...

The harbor remained behind, with its necklace of lights and its fat silhouette of love for a serious and not at all pound-foolish man. Fifty thousand souls, and a happiness so far, so far away, at the other side of the harbor —monstruous curve in the sea, the Panama canal, the Atlantic Ocean, the Grace line and the etceteras of destiny—. Suddenly —he did not know how— Paris. And sixty chapters of a novel that he had been crafting on board: —a thousand paper sheets blackened with letters that frightened Manuel's sanity, crazy things, screams, all without a reason. The American jacket of his tensed and hardened with that sheaf of hysteria and conflict. Because the novel was a conflict of hysterias —a woman threw herself at the arms of the millionaire and this one bit her in the chin—. Astral autobiography, what do I know... A soundless bus of springs and rubbers took Manuel in a throttle of darkness and quickness to the hotel. A streak of fog, cold, drizzle and benzine gas inflated the curtain and left over the window ledge a whiff of Victrola —catfish, adultery, syrup in sachets...— Thus would a stork have abandoned a child on a maiden's bed, by mistake, by exhaustion, as a joke... As in Barranco, no more and no less. He got undressed. Once naked, he did not know what to do; he wanted to go out to the street, go back to Lima, don't do anything. He got into bed —early, bored and laggard— and fell profoundly asleep. In a moment he went back to Lima, to Union Street, and it was twelve in the morning. A Hudson dirty with mud took away Ramón through a transversal street that frightened with its tremulous, half crazy windows. A mobile fig tree transited by the street dense with seminarians, hustlers and professors of geometry —a thousand gentlemen grow old, the dirty neck, the long hand—. Manuel woke up, and now it was Paris with its smell of asphalt and its murmurs of factory and its public pleasures. Manuel visited the Latin American consuls; at the Louvre, under a hot mess of colors, a sentimental *cocotte* abandoned one hand of hers —rough and dry— in the two of his, cadaverous; at the Moulin Rouge, he really sinned; at the Pont Alexandre III, a starlet from Lima was smiling at him on the border of the brim of his hat. And one day —he did not know how— he woke up in Lima, in his celestial blue blanket, under the big dumb wings of his guardian angel. Now it was Lima with its odor of sun and guano and its solitary pleasures. Manuel did not know what to do —go back to Paris, go out to the street, don't do anything... And he fell profoundly asleep once again.

The cliff plunged its scarp in fig trees, in wet earth, in irrigation ditches, in moss, in bindweeds, in Japanese kiosks, from top to bottom, from the Parish church to the beach. Suddenly twisted the sinister, rampant route. And through a covered slide —by one side, light; by the other, a grotto of artifice and an invisible madonna, and a miracle of candles that brightened up under leaks— one landed on the platform. An old tenderness played on the piano things by Duncker Lavalle, and a violin concealed the voice behind an obese Italian woman, unknown and millionaire. An old man, down below, in the sea, spritzed those curious of his bald head with the water that flowed from him, through the hands, from the round hollow arms; and the old man was an aspiration pump and two hands of a parish priest, forgiving and jovial. Here one wants to put one's own sign boards over the indifferent sunblinded doors: "It is prohibited to sin in the passageways", "We kindly ask the bathers to not speak in English", "It is not allowed to completely destroy the premises", "Etcetera". Here one is possessed by a certain frenetic culture, infantilist, experienced and bored, critical and dilettantish. Paul Morand on a sailboat, with his raceless and earless lover, on the way to Siam, like in the social pages. Cendrars, who comes to Perú to preach the enthusiasm of a Bavarian and spontaneous explorer; (lynched tourists, wheat plantations and the man who strangles his destiny.) Radiguet, parading his mistress on tiptoes, all of a sudden uglied by a heroic husband. Istrati, in a stench of Dutch cheese, a ship's hold and Eurasian misery. Everybody equal to everybody else, everybody indistinguishable, unaffiliable —secretaries of legation, inheritors of textile factories, exchanges from schools of European nuns, deferred university students, lay sisters who have come in search of health, of holy scandal, of spiritual experiment...— Excessive Baedecker[23],

---

[23] *sic.* Verlag Karl Baedeker, founded by Karl Baedeker on July 1, 1827, is a German publisher and pioneer in the business of worldwide travel guides. The guides are often referred to simply as "Baedekers"

guide of I don't know which avant-garde Pentapolis, unconfessable nationalism, tremendous gut feeling... A drunk Charleston shakes up a chubber like a sack full of wooden blocks. A policeman rubs his anointed and smutty hands. The funicular rubricates modernly the pre-republican commission of the cliff. Lima, Lima, at last... And everything isn't anything but your madness and a Peruvian establishment for sea bathing. And a *criollo*[24] and premature desire that Europe will make us men, men of women, terrible and Portuguese men, Adolphe Menjou men, with a little fake mustache and camera assistants, with an international smile and a dozen London gestures, with a determined danger and a thousand unforeseen vices, with two Rolls-Royces and a German liver disease. Nothing else. Bad Nauheim, Cauterets, the estival Paris... None of that.

She had a little parochial blouse and a very polite little index finger. Public school teacher. Twenty-eight years. Healthy thorough. Christian resignation to spinsterhood. The little face, very white. The little nose, very fragile. And some little glasses tied to the right ear

---

24. Cf. note 13, p. 54

by a lightest little gold chain. And, above all, Reuter soap —white and pedagogigal scent—. The skin of hers in the nose was finer and more sensitive than in any other part of her body, although nobody was ever able to confirm this. But, bah!... everybody also knew that she would never get married, and nobody could prove this beforehand, and, nonetheless, that was the truth. The truth!..., an enthusiasm of missionary friar, a theme of frenetic cuckold, the bad part of a good book, whatever, but not the skin of a twenty-eight year old pedagogue, right? The nose of hers was filled with difficulties by the glasses: they were a little lap dog that barked reflections. Also the modern customs and the news from *"La Prensa"*[25] made her nose furrow, but less, less... At seven in the morning, would blossom the face of hers —unbelievable, unforeseeable flower— a shrub of begonias from a green pot in her window, in the ledge of her window, in her house, in her house, in her house. Pin, pin, Saint Augustine... Then the face of hers ended above a long, secure, firm body, of guardian angel, of prudent virgin, of voluntary bachelorette. In a clumsy fluttering of sheets in her bedroom —dumb useless flapping of goose in a cage— initiated the everyday life

[25] *La Prensa* (1903-1984) was a popular newspaper of the era. Together with *El Comercio,* it was intervened in 1919 by the repressive government of Augusto B. Leguía and forced to take a pro-government editorial line.

of miss Muler, negation of the Treasury, woman of her household, domestic, lenghty, soft, intimate and cold like a bed pillow at six postmeridian. Miss Muler did everything right, with silence, with indifference, with disinclination. The cup, at breakfast, she grabbed it with the thumb and the index finger, as on a date, and the whole hand she would turn it into some vital, hard, intelligent clamps. And her index finger, more curved than ever, had therefore virtue, exoticism, smile, sadness of Russian ex duke waiting tables in Berlin. At nine in the morning, miss Muler with the strokes of the clock would in an instant become public school teacher, elementary instruction, mainstay of the State; she said no, and balled up her hands. In the afternoon, miss Muler submitted to the rumors, to the colors and to the odors, and knitted poetry with the little sticks of her legs and of her arms, ivories always anew as in the gums of an elephant. Possible follies of little bachelorette: ubiquity, crown and scepter, a celestial field, to be a bird with head of carnation, to die as a saint, to go to Paris... Asleep, she dreamed of Napoleon riding on a green horse and of Saint Rosa of Lima. She would cry only with a handkerchief. She would say: "Bon Dieu", and laughed on a scale, unwillingly. She did not comprehend Eguren, but knew him by sight. She would mumble: "By no means"... with the eyes very far away. And: "I would be glad to". And: "Jesus, Jesus...". She would place a middle and perpendicular finger over the page of the book she was reading. Etcetera. Miss Muler dreamed about him one night, three days after having met him. Preceding Ramón in turn, a colonel who was winning a War of the Pacific —a patriotic dream, of nationalistic textbook—. At last Ramón penetrated into the subconsciousness of miss Muler; and one night my dearest friend got into being a friar; he came from Palestine, in the back of mister Kakison; Lima turned into a yarn ball of towers, bell strokes were falling like stones in a labyrinth of clods; an Italian angel sang in Latin; a "boy-scout" trumpet called only the men of good will; the Jordan was escaping laughing to the sky through the half-eye of the goody-goody bridge of Viceroy Superunda; Ramón, in a Mercedarian robe and with the moon of Barranco in the hands, was appeasing the elements and coughing dreadfully. Miss Muler fell in love with Ramón. Ramón did not fall in love with miss Muler. Miss Muler was twenty-eight years old; Ramón, eighteen, but in spite of everything, Ramón did not fall in love with miss Muler. From a million points of view, in a tango long like a movie reel, a Victrola was filming in slow motion the sea resort —yellow and desolated like a Mexican village in a rancheresque photobrochure of Tom Mix—. And, behind it all, the useless and absurd sea like a booth stall in the morning that follows the afternoon of gymkhana. And a triangle of vulgar pigeons was taking away the scribbles of miss Muler in their beaks, romantically.

A big heeled German who smelled of leather and sanitary soap rented a room full of cobwebs in Ramón's house. There was another one, recently wallpapered and also for rent, but the cobwebbed one had a great window that faced someone else's garden, full of elder trees, with an Eros of gypsum and a terrible parrot over this one's head. A woodswallow that was hunting fleas in the floorboard when Herr Oswald Teller was examining for the first time, very attentively, the bedroom with the round magnifying glass of his forehead, determined him to rent it without delay, fearful that a certain Herr Zemmer or a certain Herr Dabermann would come to know that a room with woodswallows and a garden was for rent, with Love of gypsum and with sea airs. In the morning that followed that afternoon, the unbespectacled and goop-ridden eyes of Ramón saw coming down from a cart the portrait of Bismarck, the violin, the gaiters, the *Rücksack*, the seven languages, the microscope, the crucifix and the beer mug of Herr Oswald Teller, who would move residence *"mit Kind und Kegel"*[26], with all of his belongings. At last descended from the cart Herr Oswald Teller in person, fat and wet like the morning. He was coming on the side, and his diminute legs were getting entangled in the tail bristles of the mule that pulled the clumsy flatbed cart. The Lil' Martína, immense mule, old and cunning as an aunt inlaw... And Herr Oswald Teller was speaking to the cart driver about the mornings in Hannover, about the full moon, about the industrialization of America, about the battle of the Marne... and the *rr's* were coming from his stomach, and the gazes were flowing from his brain, and his memories were skidding over the blueish snow. And Herr Oswald Teller stopped his speaking cold when the Lil' Martína stopped her pulling cold. The negro Joaquin was chewing his black, fat lip, and imagining the sea, remote and perpendicular, in the sea of fog, in between the ears of his mule, with a harshness and an hermetism of a Javanese idol. The sea fog smelled like seafood, and the sea was suspended in the fog. Over the

[26] German idiomatic phrase. It has a humorous quality approximately equivalent to the English expression "with everything but the kitchen sink".

sidewalk unraveled a rain, obscure, dense, paltry, brief, of German illustrated periodicals. *"Fliegende Blätter"*, *"Garten und Laube"*[27] —magazines of covers in which there were horrible, cosmical nudes, brave jubilations of an architectural, Wagnerizing painting...— Afterwards, everything was in the room of Herr Oswald Teller. Herr Oswald Teller accomodated it all. The holler of a milkmaid fell, unexpected, in the middle of the room and, one minute later, the six bell strokes of six in the morning. The six bell strokes of six in the morning Herr Oswald Teller tucked them into a pocket of the hunting jacket, and the holler of a milkmaid he fastened it to the comb with which he combed his balding head (one day, Herr Oswald Teller said to Ramón that, when he combed it, he felt happy, smelled stables, believed he was in Hannover; and the holler of the milkmaid was still in the comb a reflection of peasant light, celestial and quiet). In the afternoons, in the long pre-nights of the winter in Lima, Herr Oswald Teller, from his mildewy room, flooded the house with music and genius. Mozart, liquified, descended the staircase and pooled in the hollows like a heavy rain that had trespassed the ceilings. Ramón raged. Classical retreat...

---

[27]. *Fliegende Blätter* and *Die Gartenlaube* were two popular German illustrated magazines. They were among the first successful mass-circulation German newspapers and forerunners of all modern magazines.

Brrr... Old music, intransigent, that is imposed on the admiration of the twenty-year-olds, by dint of warnings, of horrible grandmotherly warnings full of good sense... and Ramón stretched in his little bench, and stiffened, and listened and ended up getting dizzy, with a magic flute in the eardrums.

Lulú wore a little robe, fresh and hard like a cabbage leaf. Her face, of a spinster's doll, had the very lively colors. She no doubt had to be allowed to grow old, to discolor. One had the urge to hang her out in the sun, by the braid. Lulú was the terror of the parochial lay sisters — she sprinkled tin tacks on the benches of the temple; sprayed the holy water over the faithful women; flirted with the sacristan, disconcerted the chorus; stepped on all the calluses, extinguished all the candles... — And she was good: a pure little soul who only wanted to cheer up God with her mischief. Lulú was a saint in her own way. And in the midst of that tightened and stubborn herd of saints in the ecclesiastical manner, the savage and human sanctity of Lulú stood out as a bramble above a patch of cauliflowers.

Seafront, the last one of Barranco going to Chorrillos[28], zigzagging, marina in relief carved with a knife, a sailor's toy, so different from the Chorrillos' seafront, too much light, excessive horizon, obese sky in a sea's cure. Seafront of Chorrillos, superpanorama, with a fourth dimension, of solitude... And the whole sea varies with the seafronts —on this one, transatlantic's trip; on that one, route of Asia; on that other, the first girlfriend—. And the sea is a river of Salgari, or a shore of Loti, or a fantastic ship of Verne, and never is the sea glaucous, of livid zones, colorless, with strings of cormorants, plentiful of minimal coasts and skinny remoteness. The sea is a soul that we had, that we don't know where it's at, that we barely remember as our own —a soul that is always another in each one of the seafronts—. And the sea never is the cold and sinewy sea that squeezed from us, in its estival lusts, the childhood and the vacations. Seafront with ancient gardens of weak rose bushes and palm trees dwarfish and dirty; a fox-terrier barks at the sun; the solitude of the shanties peeks out the windows to contemplate the noonday; a worker with no job, and light, the light of the sea, humid and warm. Seafront

[28.] Chorrillos district continues along the Lima coast past the southern limits of Barranco. It's working class character stands in sharp constrast with Barranco, an upper middle class seaside resort.

with frames of dry grass, the restlessness of the first date with the girl that we did not altogether love —above this seafront there is a diverse sky, that denotes next to the sky of the sea—. Seafront with only one hour of quietude: that of six in the afternoon, the two twin skies, one, without solution of continuity, both of them with the same seagulls and melancholies.

Ample sun, hard, firm, of the ending of February. There is no possible shadow in this noonday, artificial, exact, unalterable. The night will never arrive. It is two in the afternoon, and the sun still is midway through the sky in an attraction, stubborn and silly of the earth. Glitters the gypsum of the streets —the white, the yellow, the light green, the celestial blue, the pearly gray— the perfect colors, utmost prudent, of the houses in Barranco. It doesn't smell of anything but of heat, only of heat —a solid odor of maximally dilated air—. Metals and crockeries clang in the windows. Flagpoles with no flag with a lax rope that turns into a loop on top of the cornices. The bell stroke of one o'clock undoes in the fluffy air its sludge of sound, and falls over Barranco in a flight of fledglings, mild down feather whitenesses of the hour that flew to the sea. End of lunchtime that is solitude of streets, and argentine, warm silence, and glimmering of carriageways of round auriferous stones, of riverbed stones, thirsty and covetous. A cart carries away in its squeaking and in its bumping all the fever of a strip of streets that have been traversed —nightmares, beings, banana plantations, bitterness, deaf systoles and diastoles...— The sultriness bangs isochronous the eardrums of the windows' crystals —tense, painful membranes—. And the strip, after the cart, remains pale, convalescent, with no ailment and no health. And the cart goes to the extramurals, to burn the evil of the streets in the bonfire of the remote sundown. Banana plantations in the memory... Every noise clashes with the hard air and it's a blow. Three in the afternoon. And a streetcar sings with all the soul with the guitar of the Miraflores' road, sunburst, boisterous, saddened, with two strings of steel, and in the neck of hers, the green ribbon of an alameda that whips the air of the sea. Streetcar, *zambo*[29] lothario...

---

[29] Racial term historically used in the caste class system of the Spanish and Portuguese empires. The term is used in the Americas to refer to persons who are of mixed African and Amerindian ancestry.

She shouted at me that she loved me with all her face, fresh and covered more than ever with towel lint; naked, cold and juicy in the yellow jumpsuit like the oranges on the inside; almost fell into my arms —a contrary air prevented it—; I told her she was terrifying and inoffensive like a sea lion; didn't believe me; her gluteous calves trembled, livid; I reproached her her impertinence, her immodesty, her bad faith, her seventeen years, her bare feet that could get hurt; she warned me that she bit like the rock fishes on earth, and showed me her piscinal teeth; she also knew how to claw, like the persecuted otters[30] —slowly unsheathed the not at all corneous nails: opaque hazes—; allowed me to not get scared; we went down to the beachfront, I think that by a rope, like the cats of the docking steamers; we returned to the roundabout in the water; she measured the madness in my eyes with her own; she asserted with a twirl the suspenders of her nudity on the shoulders, pallid, wanted to say to me as if to capricious children: "Be serious, or there is no luncheon...", but was afraid to make me cry. My thorax of studious boy

[30] *Las nutrias perseguidas.* In this case, the homophony between "otters" and "others" in the translation is completely coincidental, altought very suggestive. cf. note 42, p. 108

dissuaded her from my words; she forgave me; she got natural; the cold radiographed her thighs and knotted up her arms; she looked yonder the round dock; suddenly, in a stupendous, incomprehensible parabola, she threw herself into the bathers' semi-sea, head first, behind her inverted hairdo, that dangled like the tentacles of an octopus from a hook in the market. One had to wait for her on the beach, under the terrace —penumbra of marine cavern— among wholesale merchants —shivery, hairy, vertical cetaceans— and stench of seafood — green fumes—; she came out of her splash dressed in water; she no longer loved me; the two of us, under the platform; I thought of a caustic and cute jellyfish, but no...; I grabbed her by a hand that was slithering like a fish; dragged her on a painful race over spherical pebbles, up to the light and the deserted; my heels unsensitized; we stumbled the entwined hands upon an erect rail, useless, that equilibrated a silly stone on the tip, and we disengaged; she wanted to be a rail that could not be dragged through the beach just like that; a lizard of quicksilver took away one of her sad gazes; she wanted to forgive me with all her soul and I did not allow it; the dress of humidity of hers fell; she hit the beach with the knees, and said no...

On this afternoon, the world is a potato in a sack. The sack is a white, powdery, tiny sky, like the little sacks that are used to store flour. The world is swarthy, small, dusty, like just harvested in I don't know what agricultural infinitude. I have come out to the countryside to see clouds and haystacks. But I have come out almost at night, and now I won't be able to smell the tactile odors, of the afternoon, that are smelled with the skin. The sky, affiliated to the avant-garde, makes of its pulverulent whiteness, round clouds of all colors that at times resemble German balls, and at others truly clouds of Norah Borges. And now I have to smell colors. And the road I go by becomes a quadrivium.[31] And the four spur roads that the road has birthed squeal like newborns: They want to be rocked, and the wind, that, as the night comes, becomes a cabaret-going lad, does not want to rock roads: the air dresses in Oxford pants, and there is no way to convince it that it is not a man. I get away from the sky. And, upon leaving the countryside, limited by urbanization projects, I notice that the countryside is in the sky: a flock of fat clouds, the fluffiest, with

[31] *Cuadrivio.* In Spanish it can refer to a four-way crossroad or to the *Quadrivium,* a classical university curriculum involving the "mathematical arts" of arithmetic, geometry, astronomy, and music.

Exposition prizes, frolics on a green sky. And this I see it from far away, from so far away, that I get into bed to sweat colors.

The afternoons were white in the winter, and in the summer, of a reddish gold, of a crescent gold that at last became sun —a sun that filled all the sky—. The winter afternoons were white, of a luminous and overstepped whiteness of salt crystals, and the sun in them was a sun of silver with the jagged circumference. But in March there was one Monday with the rosy afternoon, an afternoon of the decadence of D'Annunzio, and all the world therein was moved by the rosy afternoon. Long rows of shivery old women (black shawls on the yellow necks of red tendons); —paunchy old men with the friend who is nobody, on the side—(cotton quotations, hairy hands with the wedding ring, and lenses, and eyeglasses, and goggles and spherical eyelids, and wrinkles that seemed like makeup). But suddenly, the rosy turned red; and the sundown was the one of everyday; and the attendance to the celestial cinema disapproved that the program had been altered. Was it not "Divine Love"[32] showing? The plot was by D'Annunzio, the hero of summertime, the red sky, the sun sky and the night like a scream. The respectable attendance withdrew kicking about ferociously, correctly, as it obliged them, people knowledgeable of their rights, serious people, honorable people. All of a sudden the sky had a "watch this" of a stallholder, and then there was no sun or summertime or anything: there only was some buttocks to the air, some tremendous buttocks reddened by a very lenghty settling. The attendance promised itself to appeal to the mayor. On Matti Street, the poplars were falling asleep quickly to wake up early. On a window, a very old piano was dying of love, like the Duke of Hohenberg —pink bald head, white sideburns— in I don't know which one of Kallmann's operettas.

We were bathing in the afternoon and the sea, to the left of the westerly point that concealed the pier as something prohibited by the municipality and that

[32] *Divino Amor.* It seems to be a reference to the classic film *Cabiria* (1914), a landmark Italian epic directed by Giovanni Pastrone, with screenplay by Gabriele D'Annunzio. For theather entrepeneurs at the time, it was not an uncommon practice to change the names of foreign films in order to appeal to a local audience.

could close down the establishment. Lalá's mom was clenching to an undone wave of the high tide, forceful wave, shaggy and clumsy like a buffalo —in the foams was searching the poor lady one of her hands that the wave was carrying away—. The day before —a malignant, cold yesterday— it was one of her slippers that got lost, when she noticed her butt-naked foot, because she stepped over a submarine gringo with it; the slipper wasn't floating anymore —since it was made of rubber—; the gringo stuck out his amorphous diver head; Lalá's mom asked for forgiveness; the gringo didn't understand; the lady made a "yes", mentally, rapidly, between two billows. The lady had found the lost hand in those of a nearby and exhilarated Turk, who due to being a Turk should not have been allowed to bathe, etcetera. Lalá showed me the nipple of one of her breasts. I hid in the sea. Lalá could now be my girlfriend. The lady surged like a submersible. Dressed in a bathing suit, she was not herself. The shanks of the breeches and the sleeves of the smock she had them swollen with water. Traversing her face, from hair to chin, the slit of a red lock of wet hairs, that she stanched with the purple tip of the tongue. A scapular cord was girdling, tightly, one of her shoulders as if for a bleeding. The old woman defied the bathing house, whipped the sea and became shadow of the shadow from underneath the platform. The ocean sea descended. Above, on a blue zone of the sky, the crescent moon blinked with the frustrated high tide. The rocks, that in a horrible noise had gotten away from the route of Lalá's mom, came rushing to our feet, very lively, familiar. The sand ran underneath —it wanted to tumble us and carry us to the high sea like sea snails—. Lalá was piercing her ears with the pinkies; her eyes and her teeth were chattering. I kissed her all of a sudden, without reason, behind an enfeebled and compliant wave that didn't keep going forward; the kiss resonated in the afternoon like in a theater. The water was black and green in blotches. The rails of the pier were breaking and unbinding from the bottom in stretchmarks of shadow, in shadows of fish, in stains of shadow... It seemed that everything was going to crumble apart —the sky with the horizon in flames; the sea, full of holes in the surf; the pier with the irons that were dissolving in the sea—. I did not want Lalá. My fingers were wrinkled, hardened. —Lalá blew upon them a wet and warm breath of a barber's pulverizer—. We came out from the bath as if from the bed, as if from a dream... Lalá yawned.

I imagine that man as a vague stature from which a poorly cut jacket dangled. Some words in the diary of Ramón attempt —in vain— to remake integral in my brain the image of that man, shattered, dispersed. "On a face of wax, the eyes of a dog, filled with a sweetness that was all indifference. And one of the index fingers —the one in the right hand, the finger of the idlers, of the chaplains, of the boys— rigid, yellowed by tobacco. And the moustache, cindery, of golden handlebars, that seemed to sprout from the nostrils like a hard smoke cloud of tar... And the pants, empty holes, curved by tremendous knee pads..." Thus states the diary of Ramón, the notebook of black oilskin covers full of words that I don't know how ended up in the hands of miss Muler, public preceptor and principal of the school center "Republic of Haiti". Oh, the hands of miss Muler...! How they moved among the writing gadgets and the cardboard grammars, rudiments of geography with angelical cleanliness, with fantastical security! But these notes I don't know if they will truly be the image of that man that was in Ramón or simply crazy things that came down to the fingers of my friend when writing his diary, transmuted in the silly fancy of signaling something. Had that man sometime existed?

Had Ramón and I dreamed it? Had Ramón and I created him with someone else's features, with gestures of his own? Had the boredom driven us to make a man? Did that man have a memory, understanding and will?... Because I see coming into order the data that Ramón speaks of right now, humanly, in a dense and yellow atmosphere of summer. I also see that man dispersed, incomplete, half madness, half environment, half truth, with the belly of wind and the calves of a marine horizon, vertical, charadesque, bamboozled, on the edge of a seafront with no railings. Perhaps everything is nothing but essential elements, physiognomical dates, crosses and capital letters, tachygraphy of a bypassing observer that at a given moment would rehash in Ramón's fat and scraggly head, the image of that man, that, in fact, existed. I feel now a desire of having before me that man to ask him the tremendous questions whose answers reveal the humanity or the inhumanity of a subject. "Are you a Leguía[33] supporter? Which brand do you smoke? Do you sustain a mistress? Do you feel the heat?" If that man were to respond that he was a monarchist, that he

---

[33] Augusto B. Leguía (1863-1932) Peruvian conservative president and *de facto* dictator from 1919 to 1930. The constant ironic references to politics in *The Cardboard House* are heavily influenced by the sociopolitical context of Leguía's government.

did not smoke because he lacked a narghile, that he loved a pious old woman, that he did not feel the heat except in the winter, then I could know with certainty that that man had been made by us, Ramón and I, in an hour of leisure and crepuscule, insofar as the sun rolled silently, very quickly, through the concave sky, red and green, like a Milanese ball. It is indubitable that there are men who are nothing but their empty pants. Children there are who are nothing but the joy of the sailing cap —children who are not even the cap they wear—. Women there are who are barely a phony hand in the donkeyskin purse. Friars who barely are one wrinkle of a cassock. What would that man be?

Postnoonday, sun fumes and a frolicking of puerile boredoms... Catita, mean heart... Nothing to be done, nothing to think of, nothing to wish for. Catita, mean heart... But, now Catita nothing matters to me. A street illuminated with silence —down it go our eyes of us, our eyes, incautious and curious children—. And we end up blind. And an air of *yaraví*[34] cools down a bit

[34] Musical fusion genre derived from the Inca *harawi* and Spanish troubadour songs. More generally, the term 'yaravi' is used to designate Andean poetry, music and songs characterized by a sweet and melancholic temperament.

of street with its breath of *puna.*[35] Afterwards, nothing, not even ourselves, you and I, Fernando, devout face and long pants.

Night, bashful and hairy dogs... Dirty desire of climbing to the trees, that in jest have blossomed a star —a bursting, mocking, buzzing bright star—; ficus, ficus, in its autumn of shadow. Fear of the bogeyman with the face of a mother-in-law. Catita, cold little bed... Streets under the electric light, the nightmare of a street cart, squatty houses with fabulous palm trees... And a silence in chunks that is a mortal sin.

Spruce morning of freshly washed foliages. Sometimes, a peasant breeze, that, rarity of rarities!, seems to come from the windows, passes by carrying a sweet smell of legumes. But she is a breeze that escapes at the first corner. And the air turns into being empty and clean and clear. A pretty *chola*[36], with the hard, sleek, wet hair —carving of mud— walks absorbed, watching how her breasts jump, how they tremble, how they jump... She's a cook. The calves, firm, ugly, browning the white cotton stockings. She has left the toddler in the kitchen. And it is certain that now she doesn't think about him: now she only thinks about herself, about

---

35. Montane grasslands ecoregion found in the central Andes Mountains of South America. It's characterized by dry weather and cold temperatures.
36. cf. note 15, p. 55

her breasts that she watches tremble, jump. Rarefied air. —In vain pass the streetcars— nothing is heard.

We read the Spaniards, nobody else but the Spaniards. Only Raúl leafed through French, English, Italian books, in translations by a certain Pérez, or by a certain Gonzáles de Mesa, or by a certain Zapata and Zapater. Thus, we had, in spite of Belda and Azorín, a picturesque image of world literature. Thus, we knew the life —eternal as that of God the Father— of that poor Stephen Dedalus —"a very interesting four-eyes and who wet the bed"—. Thus, we knew the prank that six characters played on a good theatre director, of how they tempted him to write and of how they ended up not existing. Thus, we knew of a lad who pretended to be a disciple of the Devil, as if this one would want to discredit himself into teaching. And weird names that were men —Shaw, Pirandello, Joyce— would dance in Raúl's tip of the tongue —puppets bewitched by an illiterate witch—. To know ourselves... Stephen Dedalus was not the one of Joyce: Stephen Dedalus was, no doubt, an ambitious boy who dreamed of marrying a rich Yankee; a very intelligent boy and very confident of his conduct, so much, that he deceived a monastery of Jesuits. As for Pirandello's son, he opined that it was immoral on the part of the father —a cynical cuckold— to impose on a son of whom nothing bad was said, a putative mother. Ramón was biting his lip. The Devil's disciple was a vicious and bullheaded lad, surely hairless. And we had a behaviorist concept of humanity. Joyce? An idiot. Pirandello...? Another idiot. Shaw...? A third idiot, even more of an idiot than the two previous ones, with his historic concept of literature, his failed jokes and his mania of being contrary; and on top of all, chaste, old and vegetarian; and above all, Irish, that is to say, English, despite the Pope and the "home-rule".

All of us, minus Raúl, abided by the Spanish and American literary hodgepodge. Because, as in the Barataria isle, it is a delicacy for chaplains and moneybags.

There's Wilde for the curious ones who sin out of boredom. Come the asexual confidants of don Jacinto Benavente, with pointed beard, parabolic bellies and fancy pants: their fairies, who know the customs of the good society; their adulterers by mandate of the confessor; their perfectly human and useless lives; their centripetal morals; their corny conversations, everything of Benavente's. And come also the literature of Fernán Caballero, credulous and hallowed literature, with ecclesiastical license. And the one of Pardo Bazán, that smells of an old lady's closet with vague effluviums of thyme, full of sins that don't get to be committed —a pious intention of the writer!—. And the catharral and brave of Pereda, with his severe, somber, frowning girls, who give themselves to the neighbor by the love of God. And that of Pérez Galdós, practical and perilous, with consumptives and madmen and criminals and the plague-stricken, but whom the reader sees from afar with no danger. And that of Maeztu, table of logarithms that smells of eau de cologne and in which everything fits like in a Manchester handbag, all condensed, of course, full of numerals, dignified like an English spinster. And that of Camba, railroad dialogue with a young man without family, without employment and without philosophies. And that of Father Coloma, full of prudent and scaled angels who do not leave the zither for a moment, and of good-natured courtesans, and of advice for the Catholic aristocrats. And the digestions of Baroja, and the matins of Azorín, and the vespers of Valle Inclán and the nights of Zamacois. Everything, everything, like that, as it comes as it falls, but without inhumanities...

Ramón's aunt would bathe a long time. With a thick hand, she soaked the cloth cap, and with the other, tamed the waves. Sometimes, a slipper would peek out at a stretch from her insubmergible bosom —it was a gutterpup foot—. She was an old woman who feared the rocks, fat, humidous, good summer-vacationer; she would come with the first warmth and leave with the last one. She rented a shaky little cottage with a big window and an immense translucent film. A cat that resembled a little black girl, and a little black girl that resembled a toy... The Parish behind and a phonograph of tin and wood. The little patio was a basket of yellow papers: Ramón's aunt never read the newspapers. She listened to the retreat from a dining room, in a bobble stitch robe. An old woman. Fat. She will come back in December. Ramón, on the other hand, will never come back.

Now the summer is over for real. The summer and the pretext of summer, the girls of cheerful legs, the hollow-eyed friars, the speakers of the Justice Courts, the heat, the vacations... The pretext... The pretexts... Now the winter is sneaking up on us —a winter, extracalendarial, orthodoxly Bergsonian: movies in twenty chapters—. Lima, the dirty Lima, equestrian, commercial, sporty, nationalist, so serious... Now for real is the summer over. We have come, Lucho and I, to the intermediate seafront, which we have baptized with the name of boulevard Proust. Yes, boulevard Proust —seafront, ancient, valuable, remarkable, that is not a boulevard by both sides, but only by one— at the other, psychological immensity of the sea, the sidewalk of the street in which the house of the Swann family is, the door sensed in each one of its molecules, the infinitesimal calculus of its probabilities of emotion, etcetera. Trees? —the lampposts— trunks of bushes that the light twists and the shade makes green. At six in the morning, at six in the afternoon, the lampposts are the most vegetal thing in the world, in an analytic, synthetic, scientific, passive, determinant, botanical, simplest manner. —the trunks sustain at the upper end crystal bells that enclose yellow flowers—. In the great greenhouse of the dawn, in the domestic furnace of the twilight —obscure rays, hypervegetability, observation, summary, skeleton, truth, exact temperature—. But now it is not the sea a street side of a French novel —the sea now is the sea with waves and with its bit of daydreaming for an unmarried aunt—. And moreover, with its colors —a very discreet sundown, the antithesis of an early morning that arrives on tiptoes, almost a hot little mama morning, but without a kiss or sign of the cross—. Sunday and first Mass. The organ propagates itself in the mist like a clashing of stones in the water. Today there will be a plenilune, full moon, unconstellated sky with its borehole of light in the middle —intact and glorious belly button—. We will not refrain from coming here this evening. In the coffee cup of the firmament, will float indissoluble, ungravitated, the sugar lump of the moon. And all of it, my friend, will be poetry. Us, we will prelive a superlife, perhaps truly future where all men will be brothers and abstemious, vegetarians, and theosophists, and sportsmen. And the sugar moon will for us become a horrible sweetness in the mouth. And a cloud the color of *café au lait*[37], what will it be? It's possible that it won't be anything. Or perhaps she will be a verse of Neruda. Or perhaps a coast of sign, motherland of Amara, dream of Eguren. Or if you prefer, simply a cloud the color of *café au lait* —it's for a reason we are sixteen years old and have grown peach fuzz—. Tomorrow, soccer match on the difficult turfgrass of I don't know which terrain in the outskirts of Lima. Champion of tendinous and hairy mosaic legs,

37. "Café con leche" in the original.

countenance of apterous Byzantine angelo in the cloud of dust, Romanian emigrant, tachygrapher-typewriter of the Dess firm, stock market agency... And the whole match will be the stupid and perfect designation of the advance that would stop in the air a hard black ball clutched to the ground by an invisible elastic. Summer, pathetic, niggling, implausible, cinematic, from a Pathé newsreel. A Rolls ran away snoring by the asphalted highway like a Swiss and famous bull, recently castrated. And on that Rolls went away the summer to the North Pole, taking along the superseded hope of that argentine October full of seagulls —the last October we have lived—. To be happy one day... We have already been so for three thorough months. And now, what do we do? Die?... Now you get sentimental. It is sanity to get lyrical if life gets ugly. But it is still the afternoon —a matutinal afternoon, naive, of cold hands, with westerly braids, serene and continent like a wife, but of a wife who would have the eyes of a bride still, but...— Do tell, Lucho, stories of Quevedo, brute couplations[38], sudden husbands, surprised nuns, chaste English women... Say whatever comes to your mind, let's play psychoanalysis, let's chase old ladies, let's make jokes... Everything, except to die.

---

[38]. *Cópulas brutas.* There is a double entendre between *coplas* (four-line stanzas, folk songs) and *cópulas* (copulations, sexual intercourse).

underwood poems

"Hard and magnificent prose of the city streets without aesthetic concerns

Through them one goes with the police toward happiness.

The goggle-eyed poetry of the windows is a secret of seamstresses.

There is no more joy than that of being a well-dressed man.

Your heart is a horn forbidden by the ordinances of traffic.

The houses ruminate their paces of oxen.

If you'd let it be known that you're a poet, you'd go to the police station.

Wipe the enthusiasms out of your eyes.

The automobiles rub your hips, turning back the head.

Believe they are vicious women. Thus you will have your adventure and your smile for after dinner.

The men you run into have the calloused flesh of office.

The love is anywhere, but nowhere is it in another way.

Workers pass with the eyes resentful of the afternoon, of the city and of the men.

Why would the Cheka[39] execute you by shooting? You have hoarded nothing but your soul.

The city licks the night like a famished cat.

And you are a happy man, perhaps the only happy man.

You have a shirt, and do not have great thoughts of any class.

Now I feel anger against the accusers and the comforters.

Spengler is an asthmatic uncle, and Pirandello is a stupid old man, almost one of his characters.

But I'm not to become furious because of petty things.

A thousand things have made the men worse than their cultures: the novels of Victor Hugo, democracy, primary instruction, etcetera, etcetera, etcetera.

But the men are bent on loving one another.

And, since they don't achieve it, end up hating each other.

---

39. Russian secret State Police established after the Bolshevik Revolution of 1917. The main activities of the Cheka were the persecution of deserters and the suppression of political opposition.

Because they don't want to believe that everything is irremediable.

The Greek polis I suspect was a whorehouse where one had to go with a revolver.

And the Greeks, in spite of their culture, were happy men.

I have not sinned much, but already know of these things.

Bertoldo[40] would say these things better, but Bertoldo would not say them ever. He does not get into profundities —and he's old, wants peace and even supports the moderates.

The world is not precisely crazy, but indeed overly decent. There is no way of making it talk when it's drunk. When it's not, it abhors the drunkenness or loves its neighbor.

But I do not know sincerely what is the world nor what the men are.

I only know that I must be fair and honest and love my neighbor.

And I love the thousand men that are within me, who are born and die at every instant and don't live at all.

---

40. Popular picaresque character featured in the comedies of the Italian writer Giulio Cesare Croce (1550-1609).

Here are my fellows.

Justice is some ugly statues in the city squares.

None of them I like neither little nor much —they are not goddesses nor women.

I love the justice of the women without a tunic and without divinity.

On point in honesty, I'm not one of the worst.

I eat my bread alone, without making my fellow envious.

I was born in a city, and I don't know how to see the countryside.

I have spared the sin of desiring it would be mine.

Instead, I desire the heavens.

I'm almost a virtuous man, almost a mystic.

I like the colors of the sky because it's certain they're not German dyes.

I like to walk along the streets somewhat dog, somewhat machine, almost naught of man.

I'm not very convinced of my humanity; I don't want to be like the others.

I don't want to be happy with the permission of the police.

Now on the streets there is a little sun.

I don't know who has taken it away, what bad man, leaving stains on the ground with a beheaded animal.

A crippled little dog passes by —here is the only compassion, the only charity, the only love of which I'm capable.

The dogs don't have Lenin, and this guarantees them a life human but truthful.

To walk along the streets like the men of Pio Baroja (all a bit dog-like).

To chew bones like the poets of Murger, but with serenity.

But the men have postlife.

That's why they dedicate their life to the love of the fellow.

The money they make it to kill the useless time, the empty time...

Diogenes[41] is a myth —the humanization of the dog.

The longing that the great men have of being completely dogs. The little men want to be completely great men, millionaires, sometimes gods.

But these things must be said in a low voice —I feel afraid of hearing myself.

---

41. Diogenes of Sinope (412-323BC). Controversial Greek philosopher from the Classical era. He was despectively called "the cynic" by his contemporaries, after the greek word Kynikos (dog), due to his naturalist leisurely lifestyle. He was the accidental founder of the philosophical school of Cynism.

I am not a great man —I am any given man who assays the great felicities.

But happiness is not enough to be happy.

The world is overly ugly, and there is no way of embellishing it.

I can only imagine it as a city of brothels and factories under a wing flap of red flags.

I feel my own hands delicate.

What am I, what do I want? I'm a man and don't want anything.

Or, maybe, to be a man like the otters or like the others.[42]

You do not have the ears overly big.

I want to be happy in a little way. With sweetness, with hope, with dissatisfaction, with limitation, with time, with perfection.

Now I can embark myself in a transatlantic. And go fishing during the voyage adventures like fish.

But, where would I go?

---

42. *O, tal vez, ser un hombre como los toros o como los otros.* This verse is one of the most interesting examples of Adán's wordplay in *The Cardboard House.* By rearranging the same letters in "toros" (bulls) and "otros" (others), Adán carries along the subtle opposition between Humanity and Animality that is one of the main themes of the book. Even thought it's impossible to reproduce the same arrangement in translation, we have tried to preserve some of the wordplay by using the homophones "otters" and "others".

The world is insufficient to me.

It is overly big, and I cannot shred it into little satisfactions like I want to.

Death is only a thought, nothing more, nothing more...

And I want it to be a long delight with its end, with its quality.

The seaport, full of fog, is overly romantic.

Cythera is a North American resort.

Yankee girls have the flesh overly fresh, almost cold, almost dead.

The panorama changes like a movie from all the corners.

The final kiss already sounds in the shadow of the hall full of cigarette embers. But this is not the final scene.

But that is why the kiss does sound.

Nothing suffices me, not even death; I want measure, perfection, satisfaction, delight.

How have I ended up in this lost and foggy cinema?

The afternoon will already have ended in the city. And I still feel like the afternoon.

Now I remember perfectly my innocent years.

And all the bad thoughts are erased from my soul.

I feel like a man who hasn't sinned ever.
I'm without a past, with an excessive future.
Going home..."

Ramón died when he didn't have anything left but the creeping and overwhelmed pleasure of looking under the seats in public places —movie theather, streetcar, etcetera—. One day, deep and empty, wherein one rolls from hour to hour unconscious, comatose like in a cliff from stone to stone, from rock to rock. The dirty cup of the sky was filling up slowly with sugar, iced water and lemon zest —a thirsty cloud was clicking the tongue. Died Ramón. To look under the seats... Ramón became an utmostly vicious smoker. To put out the cigarette, to flick away the ash, to sidestep the wind, to extend the arm, all of that procuressly[43] facilitated him the joy of surprising the shoes, almost in undergarments, or at a table talk, or frittering away a Sunday. Sunday of the shoes, penumbra underneath the couches, with

[43] *celestinescamente.* A reference to *The Comedy of Calisto and Melibea or La Celestina* (1499) by Fernando de Rojas. The name Celestina has become synonymous with "procuress" in Spanish, especially an older woman used to further an illicit affair.

a saturday on the back, half-light underneath a table... Table talk of the shoes; little siesta; the shafts turn loose the shoelaces; a toe cap yawns, the noonday wrinkles the leather, tired of walking all morning; the right shoe lies down on its side and snores. Shoes in undergarments; the uppers, of yellow fabric, are seen outward, intimates, like a shirt... Shoes, silent old ones, in couples, like disenchanted spouses, together at the heels, separated at the tips. The past, the marital life unites them forever and drives them apart at this hour in which they would want to be twenty years old him and her, the right shoe and the left, the male and the female, the husband and the wife —to be twenty years old and marry badly or shack up well...— The booties and the sneakers of children get together at the top, by the tips, by the face, almost in kisses, behind a fold of the nursemaid's apron. Adolescent shoes, elegant, straight, crazy, always misguided, never decently parallel... shoes in the bad age, in the dangerous age, the lungs weak and the inclinations robust... Old shoes, a soul alone in two leathers and this not loving one another... Ramón left the verses that are above, typewritten, by the index, of a book of his that I inherited with the pages still uncut.

Old shoes, a soul —a dirty layer of glue between the insole and the sole —a soul in two bodies —two swollen and rheumatic bodies of rugged leather—, a sole soul in two bodies... He and she do not want to look at their faces.

Terrible days in which all the women are one single woman in a dress shirt. Terrible days of the in-betweenlines of Zamacois, terribly serious... No, nothing by Paul de Kock, mister Kakison. Fifteen years and long pants...! No, life is a very serious thing —nothing less than a woman in a dress shirt. Don't you understand me, mister Kakison? It is possible that you will never understand me. Admirable!... So then it's in London where life is lived? That is beside the point, mister Kakison. Marina closes the window in a dress shirt every night, but that is not a sin, by the way. Why wouldn't she do it? Marina, hairy legs, bather of eight in the morning... To bathe at eight in the morning in the sea is to bathe in the cold, in the sky, in the hour. Shower of fog, massage of chills, sponges of indecision, and the scow nearby —big marine bird with the wings of folded netting, black, fatigued flying behind—. Hm... Mister Kakison, you must wash with benzine the night stains that are in your cinnamon colored robe. The night in the robe of an English accountant of the Dasy & Bully firm... What do you have to say to this, mister Kakison? All right...? That is not an answer at this time and in this country. Do say I'm in the right, and you will speak very rightly. Yes, mister Kakison; you will say something of a sanity that you will never notice.

Nighttime stroll. We have found a street hidden from the sky by grave and dense branches. Now the sky does not exist; it has rolled up like a carpet, and has been left nude the parquetry of space whereby the worlds walk —elegant society— with slowness, with silence, with annoyance. Now I love you like I've never loved you, truthfully, painfully, I don't know how... To take a walk along this street that gives us back the steps and the voices like a grotto... A streetcar shatters a corner, blasthole of light and noise. For a moment, we sound, we vibrate on this zone of night as all the things — windows, windows, windows... Now I can be a hero with the chest convex and bloody. If now I were to kidnap you, you would tear out tufts of my hair and clamor to the indifferent things. You will not do it. I will not kidnap you for anything in the world. I need you to go by your side wishing to kidnap you. Woe to the one who realizes his desire! The sea sings faraway like a chorus that approaches at the opera. Suddenly it whispers in my ears like a glass of soda that loses its gas. A piano is the whole night —ancient sorrow, corny, on four hands... Now I tell you my feeling:

— I love you because you do not love me. Your smallness orientates my hope in the pursuit of bliss. If you would grow like the trees, I would not know what to desire. You are the measure of my joy. You are the measure of my desire. Behind all the deaths, there is the jubilance of reencountering you in the earthly paradises.

Love, little thing that never grows... If a shooting star were to fall, you would pick it up, and you'd burn your hands. My love has not fallen from the sky, and that's why you don't pick it up. You are silly and cute like all the women. You laugh, and your laughter reconciles me with the night.

— Why don't you love me? You simply abandon me to the wind that passes, and the leaf that falls and the lamppost that brightens, as if by losing me you'd lose nothing. And my love at this hour is the only thing that is attentive of you. Now you disquiet nothing but my love that follows you like your shadow, wanting to look at your eyes. Love me, even if tomorrow, upon waking up, you will not remember me. Love me, the hour demands it of you. Woe to whom does not obey the time!

Beyond the night, the dawn of the morning with its odors and its colors. Beyond the night, the song of the birds ripens in the future like the fruits in the trees. Beyond the night, your thoughts choose realities to incarnate into. And my love follows you through the skyless night of this street, like the memory of a dog of yours that would had died.

Upon ending the street, utmostly urban, begins bluntly the countryside. From the ranches with their little patios and their palm trees and their bellflower bushes are falling the broom bushes, on the mounds of fluffy earth, on the walls of adobe, on the monotonous blues of the sky... Droves of asses in a dun cloud of dust, carry adobes all God's day long. Here, on this fluffy and hard soil, in stains, lie the future houses of the city, with their caked terraces, with their finespun windows of gypsum, with their living rooms with Victrola and their love secrets, perhaps even with their inhabitants —prudent moms and modern girls, madcap youngsters and industrial dads—. On a clod one guesses the face of a distant aunt —the face of one of those third aunts who one day comes for a visit to get some air, to drink a glass of iced water—. A very old jacaranda, which is a municipal inspector of ornament, retired, kills the time, so long, of this prime afternoon, making a few flowers, of a prolix perfection, that, already, finished, casts out of itself, with the impassive boredom of a mandarin in its palace of this sudden suburb. And in the horizon, a blind odor of smoke sweeps the perspective of poplars and hillocks —of a pale color of granite, almost of blues—. A dove passes low carrying in the beak a bell stroke from the Parish, and the bell stroke is a straw for the nest. A little *cholita*[44] pulls the halter of an immense mule; and the little *cholita* is not yet fifteen years old; and the mule gets hell-bent on not moving; and the little *cholita* tenses more and more the arc of her frailest body; and the mule asserts itself on the forequarters; and I want to kidnap the little *cholita* and run away with her on the mule, to the sierra, so proximate, that its cymbals scratch the skin of my nose, making me squint when I stare at her steadily. I would descend, with the little *cholita* in my arms and the mule between my legs, into a shadowy chasm full of cactuses, with a

[44]. Diminutive of chola. *i.e. little native girl.* In Spanish, diminutives formed with the suffix — ito,ita are often used as terms of endearment. Cf. note 15, p. 55

somnambulist security in the happy nightmare... And the mule has made the halter escape from the hands of the little *cholita*, and now runs, brute, bowed, curved, on a quick and deaf lope, down the road, stuck to the to the wall, not knowing where to go... And the halter that drags half sinking in the dust is the sleek and perverse irony of a rat's arse...

I have received a letter from Catita. Nothing she tells me in it except that she wants to see me with the sad face. It is a long, trembling letter, in which a nubile girl pulls love by the ears with the fingers so secure, so slow, so surgical that for torture women have from the age of fifteen until the first childbirth... Women there are who don't get to conceive ever, and these ones are the terror of death, who to take them to the otherworld, has to fight them tooth and nail, without hope of not leaving with the skeleton's bones horribly scratched: the spinsters die heroically.

Catita's letter smells of spinsterhood —of incense, of dry flowers, of soap, of gypsum, of drugstore, of milk— . Emblematic spinsterhood with tortoiseshell eyeglasses and a stiff index finger. A bow of blue tincture culminates the aspect —always inevitably partial—. A little lapdog licks the austere perfume that the blonde laces of the blouse exhale. And a blouse of poetic fabrics —little robe of madapollam—. And, moreover, as an indispensable detail, a long face whose factions, hard and weak at once, rough, useless, make the face of linen folds. Perhaps a parrot that knows the Litany of Loreto ... Perhaps the portrait of an implausible boyfriend. Perhaps an obsessive mania of knowing it all... Perhaps a virtue crowned with thorns... But, Catita has not reached yet the age of fifteen. Truth is, her fingers don't need to know how to pull on ears. Who knows if already some boy thinks about marrying her —madness of love—? Catita, taster of young lads[45], bad woman who at fifteen years of badly accomplished age, already has the spinster hands... British spinster, expert in combustion engines, propaganda section, a weird and short man, some dry and veiny hands... Do you want to be like that, Catita? What shall I do with your letter? At this hour it's for me impossible of all impossibility, to grow sad. I am happy at this hour —it's a habit of mine—. A fishing boat in the environs of Miraflores,

---

[45] *Catita, catadora de mozos.* Catita's epithet *catadora* (taster) is an obvious wordplay with her name, but it also suggests *cazadora* (hunter). *Mozos* (lads) is a rather archaic and formal term for "young men".

salutes with the white handkerchief of its sail, so useless in this immobile atmosphere, cute, as if painted by a bad painter. That salutation is a salutation to nobody, and that joy, joy of folly, of smallness, of return, of humility... My cigarette draws admirably, and it is jubilance of a childish game, with balls and rings miniscule and blue; and it is the campestral peace of an odor of burnt stubble. See Catita? You don't see anything because you're not with me on the seafront; but I swear to you it's like that. To me, in the afternoon, in front of the sea, my soul gets good, small, dumb, human, and it becomes cheerful with the fishing boats that deploy the jest of their sails, and with the ember of the cigarette — blushing little child who loses the head in a blue toy store. And the high seagulls —black flies in the bowl of watery milk in the sky— it makes me want to scare them with the hands. When I was five years old and didn't want to drink my milk, I would drown in it the flies that I trapped with the spoon, which was a net tightened by the light until it hardened, and the flies in the milk would become propellers. And now, all of a sudden, I feel like a terrible child, and I refuse to drink the cup of milk in the sky because it does not have any sugar. And it's possible that my Momma Totuca would come, sweet Buddha of ebony, with the sugar dish where there was painted a male monkey dressed as a pirate and a female monkey dressed as a Dutch maid, who were making a connected reverence over the blue stripe that traversed the belly in all its roundness... Perhaps your star would sweeten if I sweetened the sky with sugar — your star, so bitter; your star, spinster that falls in love with the impossible comets; your star, that leads you throught bad pathways of love—. Have you heard, Catita? I cannot grow sad at this hour —at this hour, the only one in all of the day's hours in which I'm happy, unconscious, like the children; my hour of foolishness; my hour, Catita—. You tasted Ramón, and he did not taste bad to you. Well then, I will be Ramón. I make mine the duty of his to kiss you in the wrists and to look at you with the stupid eyes, worthy of all the delights that Ramón had. Dumb and winged duty, accepted on an insular, celestial, windy, open, desolate hour. I will be Ramón for a month, two months, all of the time you can love Ramón. But no: Ramón has died, and Ramón never had the sad face, and above all, you have already tasted Ramón. Yes, Catita, it's true, but I am not a sad man. Just as I am at this hour —dumb and cheerful— this is how I am almost all of the day. I am a smiling boy. I was born with the cheerful mouth. My life is a mouth that speaks, that eats and that smiles. I do not believe in astrology. I accept that there are sad stars and cheerful stars. I even affirm that the sad stars are an excellent motive for a fourteensyllable sonnet. But I don't believe that our life has any relationship with the stars. Ah, Catita! Life is not a river that runs: life is a pond that gets corrupted. In the daytime, the same trees, the same sky, the same day is reflected in it. In the night —always the same stars, the same moon, the same night—. Sometimes an unknown face —a boy, a poet, a woman— is reflected —so much more somber as older the puddle is— and the face afterwards dissapears, because not eternally a face is going to be contemplating itself in a puddle. And the face contemplates itself. And the puddle barely is a murky and mediating mirror. An old man is a puddle to which no girl goes to look at her own face. Because one's own life is a puddle, but the life of others are faces that come to look at themselves in it. Yes, Catita. But some lives are not a puddle, but a lake, a sea, an ocean where only the sky and the mountains, the clouds, great ships look at themselves. Thus, the life of Walt Whitman —a half crazy Yankee who, because of that, was an excellent poet— was an ocean full of transatlantics. That of Napoleon, on the contrary, was an ocean full of warships and of cetaceans. That of Saint Francis, a pylon in which a little donkey with a dove on the forehead would drink. That of Phillip the Second, a Dead Sea with a very sad aspect and a sinister legend. That of Puccini, an alpine lake, white with canoes from the Cook agency. That of Bolívar, a canal dangerous of pitfalls and fearful of floating barrels. Your life, a washbasin in which an armful of broom bushes soak, the odor and color of sulfur. Thus is the soul, Catita — either enemy water or a stupid water— lake, sea, swamp, washbasin full of water. But never a current with its direction and its channel. My life is a little hole dug in the sand of a beach by the hands of a truant child; a miniscule and malignant little puddle that distorts from top to bottom the image of the gentlemen who berate the truant children, the image of the respectable gentlemen who come to the beach and infest the airs of the sea —so clean, so brilliant— with their horrible odors of office. Thus is my life Catita, a little puddle on a beach, now you see I can't grow sad. The high tide undoes me, but another truant child digs me out again in another point of the beach, and I do not exist for a few days, and in them I learn always anew the joy of not existing and of resucitating. And I am the truant child who digs his life in the sands of a beach. And I know the madness of opposing life to destiny, because destiny is nothing but the desire we feel alternatively to die and to resuscitate. The horror of death for me is nothing but the certainty of never being able to resuscitate, that eternal getting bored of being dead. Ah, Catita, don't read sad books, and the cheerful ones don't read them either! There is no more joy than that of being a little hole full of seawater on a beach, a little hole that undoes the high tide, a little hole full of seawater in which a little paper boat floats. To live is nothing but to be a truant child who does and undoes his life in the sands of a beach, and there is no more pain than being a little hole full of seawater on a beach that gets bored of being so, or of being one who gets undone all too soon. Catita, don't read the destiny in the stars. They know about it as little as you do. Sometimes coincides the little puddle of my life with the plumb line of one of them, and more than one I have had sincere and plenary in my drop of water. Catita, the stars don't know anything of what pertains to girls. They themselves are perhaps nothing but girls with boyfriend, with mom and with spiritual direction. What you decipher in them is nothing but your own concerns, your joys, your sorrows. The stars have, besides, an overly provincial beauty, I don't know... overly naive, overly truthful... The poor things imitate thyne ways of seeing. Your star is, without doubt, nothing but a star who sees as you see, and its blinking is nothing but fatigue of seeing in a way that nothing has to do with its feelings. Catita... Catita, why does your destiny have to be in the sky? Your destiny is here on Earth, and I have it in my hands, and I feel a terrible desire to throw it into the sea, above the railing. But no. What would you be without your destiny? Your destiny perhaps is to be a little puddle on a beach of the sea, a little puddle full of seawater, but yet a little puddle in which there is, not a little paper boat, but a little fish thrown into it by a fat and brute wave.

Sergio... He had a name that did not suit him... a serene and chaste name, with a touch of the steppe, fatality and popery. He was a boy of porcine eyes who sometimes, in his malice, had the stares of an ape, small, acute and black. All of him was in his skin, of a coldness and a hue and a smoothness and a light of amber. He also was in his head which was a topknot of curly and hard brown hairs on the bald forehead. I cannot remember him except as one who passes very rapidly through a populous street, hunkered, wired, hiding the face in the haste. He also was in the sound of his heels when walking, colorless sounding, dry, of knocked wood. Sergio was in his whole figure. It was impossible to know more about him: Sergio lied like no other, with the whole soul, beyond truth and plausibility, beyond... And like so, always. One day, Sergio got into being a friar. And nothing else has been known of him. Eugenio D'Ors, distinguished Dominican philosopher, can write down his life, Sergio's or his very own, with holy hope of figuring out with certainty why got into being a friar a boy who had the eyes of a pig and who lied like no other. And D'Ors could even recount his death to us beforehand —that of Sergio— under a crucifix big and cruel as death itself, himself grasping from a word so simple of solitude and with the whole morning in the peephole of the cell. And he could add fat subtleties to the simplicity of the death of an old bearded friar who once upon was young and very sexual. Oh what a wonderful book could Eugenio D'Ors make out of Sergio's life and death! How fitting for an unmotivated and stupid life, the rosy philosophy, so very naive, so Catalonian, of the Glossator! It seems to me I'm reading him: "...and thus... But let's examine, Glossator, and may love not drag us down... Measure... Compare..." But, I don't know why, I believe now and then that Sergio never died; that, at the hour of death, he will play dead; that he will let himself be buried and that, after two days, he will unearth himself and return to Lima to tell lies about the monastery and to begin a new life. Hopefully it will be so... But the book of Eugenio D'Ors could not then be written, and I could never get to know how Sergio was.

He would grab one of her hands of hers. She would cram a fat leg, whichever, almost someone else's, under the right of his, contracted like in a dropkick. The face of his would ignite in red as a traffic lamp or a night shift drugstore. Suddenly, this one would gyrate and a face identical to the previous one but yellow would appear. It was the stopping signal. She remained impassive like a harlot. Smiled candidly, sunk the leg more and bit her lower lip without blinking. Ramón was getting skinny. She was getting fat. Ramón was a beast who was beggining to make ideas. She was a woman who was starting to bestialize. All of a sudden the sun would ignite with a terrible, carmine warning light. Thundering passed the railroad of the night. She and Ramón were getting into the last wagon. Into a sad and obscure freight wagon.

She was a fierce taster of young lads. All of us had to roll the head over her hard and round little chest. Thus, from this inevitable love, we were making an era —"When I was wooing Catita..."—. But it was Catita who was wooing us. When looking, she winked the eyes without noticing. Her eyes, round like her whole self... And the name she didn't say it right. That antepenultimate "i" elongated, overshadowed, warded off, her, near, round, cheerful. And above all, infatuated. Catalina is a gothic name; makes one think of ogives livid with crepuscules, of fountains of mossy bronze, of hectic Rhenish boroughs, of knotted chastity belts... And Catita was a blond window of noonday; a pile of white cement, modern, pulchritudinous; a hefty cloth umbrella for the beach; a schoolgirl's crazy hair ribbon... Lalá, behold her name of hers[46]. But Lalá was a quick and sleepless girl. Lalá, Lalá, Lalá... Soft heart and eyes of a doll, and face of laughter. Ramón threw himself into Catita like a swimmer into the sea —from bottom to top, first the hands; then, the head; at last, the feet, flexed, unheeled.

---

[46]. *He aqui su nombre de ella.* The double possesive in the sentence is intentionally cacophonic and technically incorrect from a grammatical standpoint. The breakdown of grammatical conventions can perhaps be attributed to the author's emotions regarding Catita.

On the pole of the month of January, greasy still with dirty cold clouds, Ramón ended up in sky, in air, in between, in equilibrium, in bathing suit, at the tip, with a hundred tremulous boys behind who were rushing him, upon Catita, sea. Ramón fell badly, bellyflopped, headfirst, aspersing all of us, unprepared, observers. Catita, sea for bathing at twelve in the morning with the big dumb sun on the head, dissect butterfly, litterfall of jaundice or yellow rubber cap. Catita, sea with waves so there won't be old women, so there will be boys... Catita, C note on a semicircular harbor, bannering of cities... Catita, subtle limit between the high tide and the low tide... Catita, sea submissive to the moon and to the bathers... Catita, sea with lights, with seashells, with paunchy little boats, sea, sea, sea... Or also love in which there were not old women, or big straw hats, or advices, or crossing oneself... Catita, love, with slow and fat hopes, love that with the moon goes down and up, love round, love near, love for submerging into it, for diving in it with the eyes open, love, love, love... Catita, sea of love, love of sea. Catita, anything and nothing... Catita, all the vowels[47] appearing in her, thorough, integral, in body and soul in the a and disappearing

[47]. Cf. the poem *Voyelles* (Vowels) by Arthur Rimbaud.

little by little, trait by trait, in the others; in the e, tender and silly; in the i, skinny and ugly; in the o, almost her, but no... Catita is honest and pretty; in the u, cretine, albine... Catita, some consonants, so similar to the b in the hands, to the n in the eyes, to the r in the gait, to the ñ in the character, to the k in the ingenuity, to the s in the bad memory, to the z in the good faith... Catita, round field in the sea, round kiss in the love... Catita, sound, sign... Catita, any given thing and the opposite precisely... Catita, in the end and after all, a cute girl, truthful, lively, coquettish as she could be... To grab her was as impossible as compressing with the tip of the index finger the water jet in the mouth of a large spout; hard flesh to the touch by the pressure, flesh that escaped through the slits of the fingernail, through the streaks of the skin; that leaped to our face; that, if deposited into a container, still, was but dense light, water that could be drank and in which little paper boats could be thrown in. Water, water, water... And, in the end and after all, an infatuated cute girl, taster of young lads, Catita...

On the rooftop, the unique and multiple air, all of itself resolving itself in currents invisibly like Bulgarian milk in bacillum; on the rooftop, to the dense air of sun rubbers, of colorless mucilages of humidity; —on the rooftop— the missus' panties. It's in the humidities, bluer the blue of the sky, and if an innominable bird passes behind them, it grows and grows as through a magnifying glass. It's a window of the single floor that the house has: oniric vision looming to the ambience, stunned, dirty, crazy, of the crystals whitened by an oblique afternoon reflex, the gentleman's waistcoat with the silver chain and the watch hidden in the pocket. Through the same one, peeking out, instead of the gentleman's flesh affirmed by the gentleman's clavicles, two stripped little balls that culminate the backrest of the Vienna chair. Old bones, already with the terrified color of skeletons that are exhumed after long years of interment... My back to the sun, I open with the shadow of my head, a dark capiciform hole in the crystal light. There they are, without horrors of nightmare, the waistcoat and the chair, human, familiar, spontaneous, frank, at home. The potbellied gentleman. The cashmere of his waistcoat, that billows from below, jokingly urges the straw mat to fatten up, to deploy him, to fill him up... The straw mat, skinny, pious, bachelorette. The waistcoat is buttoned up minus the last button, whose corresponding buttonhole has the round and empty malice of an old man's eye; veracious eye, sexual, to the air like the missus' panties on the rooftop... The waistcoat would be a sixty-something drunkard, cynical, womanizer, clumsy —if he had a nose, he would have it red, greasy, hairy, blighted with pimples—. In a silence that sounds brusque, sudden, violent, we might believe we hear the tick-tock of the clock, ruthless and obstinate heart of the waistcoat. The chain arches and doesn't express anything —thus, almost horizontal, relaxed, it is the waistcoat's conscience—. The straw mat is seating on the wood of the chair with the most austere decency, as in church or in a conference about domestic hygiene, the bosom and thighs on a right angle. She has eliminated of herself the belly, the breasts, the legs, out of shame; the arms, we don't know why; the face, out of decency. She has impeded sin by subtracting herself one dimension. That's why we imagine the straw mat —two ascetic round lividities— with a little curl of hair on the forehead, to drive away the bad thoughts; with a single white hair in the topknot, of black lacquer, for remembering death when looking herself in the mirror; with a mole on the tip of the nose, we don't know what for; with a Latin ejaculatory prayer on the lips for avoiding the useless words. The day cackles. A hen cackles like the day —secret, unobtainable, manifest, discontinuous, extensive—. A frond rubs itself with a house, under protest of chaste sparrows. Above, the sky, cirrous. Below, the street stained neatly, energetically with light and shadow as with soot and chalk. The gentleman's waistcoat belches, swells up and, at last, belches. The sweepers make with their brooms, acute and scraggly as paintbrushes, those drawings on the tree-lined streets. The sweepers have hairstyles of aesthetes, eyes of toxicomaniac, silences of litterateur. There are no penumbras. Yes, there is one penumbra; a gas of light in vain dilates through the street that lenghtens and flees to annul it. Here is not the shadow the negation of light. Here the shadow is ink, it has upon things an inappreciable dimension of thickness; it dyes. The light is a floury and albous powder that the wind spreads or takes far away. A raggedy slip of a girl skewers on a strand nude spools of thread. I skewer adjectives of timber on the rough and thick string of an idea. At the bottom of the street, closing it, grows pale a blue wall until it is the sky itself. This city is positively not a village. The jackasses devoutly respect the sidewalk. The jackasses who only bray at hours determined by the neighborhood... The jackasses who do what one doesn't speak of, behind a tree or a post without lifting the leg... The jackasses who do not dare to graze on the shrubs of couchgrass and beggarweed at the borders, cemented, of the ditches... the jackasses who, by the side of the roadway, browse in the low branches of the cart driver beheading trees... Oh, the jackasses, who are the city's only villagey thing, have become municipalized, bureaucratized, humanized...! The jackasses earn merits to obtain the electioneering rights, those to elect, those to be elected. On a stench of refried and kitchen, a world enclosed in this world is unveiled to me —the world of the corral—. The roosters also become humanized, though not like the jackasses —in a sane, civic, sensible manner—, but rather in a strange, impertinent, exotic way. Not to become men but Englishmen. Now it's the roosters, eccentric gringos who dress in Scottish wool, practice stupid sports like worm hunting, play golf with gnawed bones and cobs of corn, trembleconstantly from the cold, wake up in the early morning and do not understand females. Soon they will smoke a pipe, read magazines, play polo, gentlemen on a cat, and will depart on a pleasure trip to Southampton on a P.S.N.C. ship. The hens are good mothers who are bent in still being to the husband's liking. The morals of the corral decay. If it wasn't for the solid good faith and the austere customs of the ducks... If it wasn't for the civilist and clerical traditionalism of the turkeys — scant cleanliness, bad odor, preterition, juridical frock coat, the droopy snood, great-great-grandfathers who were counts, mortgages... The female ducks don't know of these things —the husband, the grocery, themselves, the house and the children; one must eat well, practice the virtues and save up for old age.

The ducks would reprobate of Nansen's trip to the North Pole. The ducks —I don't know why— always seem to be on a quarrel with a blood aunt over a damned inheritance. The ducks we don't know if they descend from meridional emigrants or from some fantastic French consul, married to a Paraguayan lady and settled in Lima, where he died in 1832 or in 1905. The Rabbits have the ears long, as we all know, but they're good people. Little is known about them, always well dressed, mind you, but they live in a cave. A fact also: They read Pitigrilli. We would say that they're secondrate people, nosey, meddlesome, know-it-alls, with bastards in the ancestry... Soon they will acquire a late model Ford limousine, and a second hand pianola. The girls are rather prettyish. There will be hebdomadary receptions. Where does the money proceed from? From nothing honorable, no doubt. That the fortune has come underhandedly is the vox populi. The friendship of the rabbits is highly sought by everybody. If they're not decent people, absolutely decent, the rabbits, their friendships will be revoked. The rabbits winked the alcoholic eyes, russeted by the sun and hide their Semitic mouths. The geese are provincial moneybags, always passing through. They have the misgiving gaze; the accent, from the sierra; the gullet, full; the family, in the plantation... They never give alms. He and she... exemplary spouses. The two of them, obese. Sometimes, a goat, naughty head, naughty head, naughty head... makes esses of a night owl while walking. He's photophobic, like a good noctambulist. The age? They don't have any. Twenty years... Fifty years... The madcaps are not an age but a character; not a personality, but a vice... or many vices. A face in-between Mephistopheles and Uncle Sam. He could have had a government job, and doesn't have it, the devil of a goat. He's a cuckold, but he's not married. He makes bitter philosophies about marriage. There's nothing as sweet as having no duties. Long live leisure, the good life!... The goat gets bored; the goat gets bored; the goat gets bored. The guinea pigs, all of them, females and males, are females. They are the servants of the male and female turkeys. They have the face swarthy, small, the eyes bright and small, the stature curved and small, the gait lively and small. Only they remain from the colonial shippon that Castilla[48] disbanded. The turkey poults call them mommas. The horses stew the old criollo dishes, they have lactated the turkey mother, they have unsnooded the turkey father, they know all the secrets of the family, they underestimate the ducks and never go out to the street because there is no money to buy a new mantle. They resemble old little black women, proverb-spouters, prayer-reciters, hot-tempered, blabbermouths. The doves are the scandal of the corral. The doves know French, they're indecorously sentimental, they go alone everywhere and there's something of cocottes in them. Their coupletists' Yankee tastes, make them revel for the tenth floors, they incite the pigeons to dress up in white and to not take care of the children.

The backcountry, sanguineous with green blood. Green are the cheeks and the lips of some of the figurines' caprices as well. Fat face of the countryside with the pale brown eye of a puddle that laughs, idiotic. The other eye —the right one— is the sun, in living flesh and with no pupil. This landscape has been five months in a madhouse jumping on one foot and disheveling

48. Ramón Castilla (1797-1867) Peruvian politician and military leader. He was the president of Perú during the economic boom of the 19th century. Castilla's governments are remembered for having abolished slavery and modernized the State.

itself with ten grappling black fingers. This landscape, hysterical, masochist, with a history of syphilis... This hoarse, bruised landscape... This landscape, one-eyed and sexless... On its belly, naked, the ecchymosis of a plowed patch. On its forehead, livid, the hump of a glade. Over its chest, like a scapulary, rare fetish, the mania of a church. The rain allays the crazy landscape. Its visions are now meek, sane, almost true; the afternoon, bovine, dicey, is beating on its opaque flanks, the coarse hindquarters with a heavy tail of sunbeams, straight, yellow. And a cow, real as nothing, behind a mud wall, stitches with mooings the tattered grass.

I dream of an iconography of Ramón, that would allow me to remember him, so plastic, so spatial, plastically, spatially. Of Ramón I only have left the grave bitterness of having known him and the permission to leaf through his intimate diary in Miss Muler's scatterbrained little alcove, a trail of cigarette butts in the city's longest street and a way of thinking and seeing that enables me to live in the midst of this amorphous grouping of houses, on these streets in encaustics, on these naive trees, on this sea half maple, half lagoon, on this plane that suddenly acquires three dimensions and ten thousand inhabitants. Oh, the sea! Only the sea has not ceased to be long waves, black, pencil lines neatly equidistant from the thousand curves of the beach. The sierra is not seen sideways but from above, the high mountains in level curves; the hills, with craftmanship. Precise obsession of chains and proyections, of scales and numerals. Blessed be Ramón, the madman who taught me to see the water in the sea, the leaves in the trees, the houses in the streets, the sex in the women. Around here has stayed Ramón made into lines, lights, secrets, aspects, ornamentations, details, wisps of grass, bell strokes... No, no. An iconography, an album in sepia and black, in two tones, by whose pages he would pass, with his melancholic big mouth, with his elusive eyeglasses, with his terrible insignificance, on the way to anywhere. Or stopped before rust-covered storefronts, or under green lampposts, or against yellow twilights. Or sitting on the parochial pupil benches, or on the drunken stalls of the seafronts, or on the slippery armchairs of the electric streetcar. Or chasing girls of gelatin and organdy, or fat shadows, or illuminated windows, or sullen dogs. With one leg stretched, or with the two legs together and firm. Inapprehensible, but indubitable, unmistakable. On the difficult afternoons of light or of tedium I would open the album and ask Ramón: What do I do now, friend of mine? And he would answer as in the happy days of his life in the Sierra: —Do what you want. And I would do whatever I wanted —go down the streets that at that hour smell of molasses syrup and kitchen scrubber—. Under the convex sky —lemon peel turned backwards— grow the rumors until becoming visible, the trees whet their branches in cypress fashion and an old man who passes sounding the pavestones with a little iron cane, drags along the floor like a cape, his formless shadow. An automobile has passed at fifty miles per hour, speed expressly prohibited, on a street through which only donkeys loaded with sandbags transit. The mayor is now hardly the gentleman with the pointed beard who must be obeyed by everybody. Yesterday the sun came out ten minutes after the hour in which it should have come out. Something else: it entered through the only part by which it shouldn't have entered: in between the ears of the last baker's donkey that in the city we have. The cold has the muscles long and white like one of the rickety athletes that sometimes carry off the trophy in the championship, homunculi with a height of three feet and the hands of a female typist. The air rubs the sky and leaves it scratched as a diamond scratches a crystal. I do what I want. A dove has carried away my last good thought. Now I am as I truly am, clean, asiatic, fine, bad. Now I wear a round rubber neck. Now I jump over above an old woman who examines her shoe on the street, a poor purblind old woman. Ramón loved the kitchen maids who give themselves to the sons of the family in the barn, on the cribs of straw and bricks for the clucking birds. The bells of Saint Francis humming a light little song —lest the prior hears them—. A zone of sky is crumbling over a corner of the sea, nearer to the island. A double and closed window —gesture of a decent household, wink of an apothecary's spectacles. In it will appear when nothing can be seen, in the night, a face that is cute, cute, cute...

The pavestones —submitted to the helioteraphy of noonday, sprawled, the face to the sun. On the street's gallery —the picture windows of air have opened—, the policeman is a room physician who observes, who observes... There is among the pavestones only one interesting clinical case —a triangular one on the corner, on the intersection of the two sidewalks (Miss C.V. of twenty three years of age and consumptive parents. Miss C.V. swallows saliva. Miss C.V. has the eyes closed. Miss C.V. is dying. Cancer of the uterus?... The name of the malady is not known. Miss C.V. is a very interesting case). The rest of the pavestones are algias, itis, osis, terribly general —married or widowed ladies who, to prolong the hour, prolong the convalescence. When one cannot have a lover because one is sixty years old, the best is to be in the sun with the eyes closed forgetting the living or deceased husband. These sexual hours of the digestion and the dinner... Good time of the sanatoriums. The one across the street, the one of the shadow, is a shim of diseased ones of the male sex, of an allusive and tragic male sex. In the heads, obscure, painful, pounds the fever of business. Through the arteries and the veins, wagons come and go. In the ears scream rings of telephones. The odor of the disease, odor of taste of bile, becomes an odor of office —odor of cedar and paper in blocks. A buzzard, with its hunched, sallow fortitude of diabetic Norwegian, departs to a station of altitude in the Swiss sky, which has already ignited for the tourists its ices, its snows, its hotels..., management of an oil company, fifteen years of equatorial sun, Venezuelan, xenophobe... readings of the Bible, quietest black beer, the Swedish gymnastics, a prolix getting unaccustomed, the scanty, stern pleasures of a preseptentrional émigré to this America, luminous, caliginous, brute, hard, mineral, myocenical, maritime... The cobblestones are stones carved with a hammer. The sun is killing them, but they do not complain. I don't know why they are here, suffering with no pay. Twenty doggies with neither breed nor tail (big ears, of sheepskin, the hanging ones; of felt, the erect ones) hurry up their statures that go from the waxy color of new straw to the bluing of steel, after a big purebred bitch and with a tail, a face, mundane, woolly, opulent... The dogs glide with the shortest, agilest rows. The sun turns all the dogs into badgers. Hunger of the great female... The social revolution... Princess Alexandra Canoff, who runs down this street, almost of Tsarskoye Selo for how solitary and solary, your Paris follies are already over... Freud, in the coprophile odors does not include those of Caron, those of Coty... This bitch smells like "Nuit De Noël", like "Night of Siam", like I don't know what night, only so as not to say good with the afternoon. How good that of giving night names to the perfumes. All the perfumes are nocturnal. Sometimes I believe that the flowers exist only so as to temper the excitement of the day. In the deserts becomes Libyc, Saharic the same sun that in these rosebush gardens is barely a jovial and promenader Barranco sun; this matchmaker sun, without family, confirmed bachelor, gossipmonger of the five continents; pretexter; this gallant sun that gives the arm to the forsaken aunts in the promenades... The flowers absorb light and heat with the carbonic gas in the assimilation. At night, wherever there is a flower, there is also a gnomic light with a tender halo of heat enclosed within the cocottish[49] little screen of each corolla. The sea also is the outskirts of the city. Now the sea is a mirror where the sky is seen, a thick and vast crystal quicksilvered with mullets and corvinas. The sea is green because the sky is green. The sky, immense face, without features and green. The sea can be a pictoric sea, ingenuist, full of fish. But now it is a mirror. The sky can be an agricultural or livestock field. But no; now it is a face that looks at itself in the mirror of the sea. A heartsick lamppost on a street that could have been and was not...; on the offshore, a stump of sidewalk, and that spirit of fluffy desire, of all the streets. A rooster turns to me on a cruel, mechanical flexion, its shaved head, the ivory and acute profile, the ears carmine, Britannic. The sea hoists tarred birds and bundled waves on the crane of the rust-covered island. The opaque marine suntrap —sun glares oxidized by the water— trickle of oil at a given moment, suddenly, long stain of mercury that casts away, that sinks... A mine of the great war, a broken egg of the "Moeaee"[50]... I don't know what

49. *cocotesco.* This adjective is a neologism from the French *cocotte.*

50. It seems to be a reference to the cosmic egg of Greek mythology, from which the Moirae/Fates and other divinities were born.

unforeseeable slope on the streets takes me always to the outskirts of the city. The sea is the outskirts as well.

The afternoon proceeds from this long-winded, motley, sluggish mule. From her emanate, in radiations that invisibilize the illumination of three postmeridian and reveal the linen of the atmosphere —a cinematograph screen, but round and without a need for a shadow—; from her emanate all things. At the end of every sheaf of rays —a house, a tree, a lamppost, myself. This mule is creating us by imagining us. In her I feel myself solidary in origin with the animate and the inanimate. We are all images conceived on a ample and supple chunk, images that foliate, or emplaster and fenestrate, or dress in denim, or top themselves with a skullcap of glass. Cosmic logic distinguishes us all in undefined species of a single genus... A window and I... A dove and I... At each step of the mule —twofold step, unalterable rotund of eternity, predetermined by a divine genius—trembles my being to destiny unbeknownst. At this moment never has the mule existed. The mule has been annulled behind a corner. Now the afternoon is itself—atheist, autogenetic, romantic, liberal, desolate—. These famished dogs, gnawers, aphonic with spine bones, dermic, enarched, from the sierra, look like cats, stray cats with realist eyes, social, enlightened, herbivorous. A gust of wind unrolls a Chinese flag, of supreme elevation, like a parchment, from the left to the right — the flag veils a rectangle of sky, where the sun precisely is—. The afternoon blackens, and the night becomes. The poles, on these streets of low and saltpetrous walls, have a violent appearance of pedestrians. The day, with its invariable humor of rain, stops them at its fourteen hours, on the edge of the sidewalks. The night just fallen, the posts set out to walk. Summer nights, poured like dark beer with starstrucking tan foams... The poles have worked a lot, grew tired, were widowed, the only son went to Guatemala... Their arms already falling down out of sheer old age. If they have not hunched up their stature, is because their bones are made of wood. Elderly electricians with the hands dried and gnawed by the gutta-percha and the balata, by the battery salts, by the gasolineous tools... They have retired, and have acquired, along with the joy of full salary and the right to act crazy, certain lines of ex-public servants in disgrace with the current government, of survivors of the remotest battles, of crackpot uncles who herborize or collect mail stamps... Between a pole and another pole, there are eighty feet of a distance that never wanes nor grows —the poles neither love nor hate each other... misanthropy, misogyny, at most a grumble of annoyance or a greeting from one to the other, and this because they can't stop doing it so... At night the poles set out to walk. I have recognized on a very remote street a pole who spends the entire day standing at the door of my house, with the hat in the hand, stiff, absorbed, as if keeping quiet about a kidney ache or doing math in the head. The poles never get together. The distances on these strange promenades are not altered —they tie them up to their waist like a rope, alpinists of the mortal alp of their lives at twenty-five degrees below zero—. We suppose in them the reckless daring of those men without little pleasures or any family —some count Godeneau-Platana, pederast and Egyptologist; some prince Giustati, Castillian and aesthete; some Mexican millionaire suddenly impoverished by a revolution... On the following morning (the mornings always follow) the poles go back to the locations of their manias. And there they are, while fourteen revolving hours go mutating the color of the air —long, skinny, erect, rigid, guessing if it will rain or it will not rain—. A pole is called Julián because he lets his beard grow... the beard, of paper streamers from the carnival of the year

1912. Another pole is called Matías, because that is his name. A poor asthmatic pole on Mott street dreams of buying an overcoat of French cloth. There are poles who pamper dogs. There are poles friends of beggars. There are European poles with green eyes of crystal insulators. There are light poles. There are telephone poles.

An ice-cream man's horn gave the tune to a nocturnal howling of dogs, symphony of tin and moon, thing torn apart from the beggining that through the gash allows us to see canine palates, black, bristled with taste buds as hard as calluses. If this way of chanting was to be melographed, it would have to be done on a temperature sheet, on graph paper, with a broken line, with odd numbers. Skeleton of music. Forty-two degrees Fahrenheit, mortal fever. A whirlwind of light and dust ascends to the sun on a terrain enclosed by thick adobe walls. A creeping air that rears up moves the whirlwind from the bottom up contracting it without folding it. Hidden air, child, prisoner... Above the big cornice of mud, after it, bad kite, the upper funnel broken around its axis of wind, elliptical circumference of inclination, clear closed curve. At night this street will be another.

Around here we will pass without knowing where we go. At noonday, the steps do not sound. The shadow goes along one's side, dwarf, unformed, silhouette of a ratty hoodlum feinting to attack. The silence closes its parenthesis on every window. Ramón, shaving soap, green blanket, holy palm on the bed's headboard, and on the window, badly open to the heat of a yellow sky —Oh, second floors in a flat town!— a leaking eucalyptus that lets round minutes fall on the painted ditch, weightless balls of charred paper, burnt and rolled leaves —homemade remedies, ancient recipes, repose, repose... Sweaty and dark-skinned girl, very ugly suddenly in a gesture, pretty if you submit to the light on the edge of the sidewalk, fume of summer, a nap dream... You make my steps keep rhythm with yours. I do not know what to tell you. Sudden blow of cold hair changes our life. You dissappear at every instant of my conciousness, and on returning, you're warm, like the hat or a book we forgot in the full sun when we fled to the shadow. The wide street opens up our eyes, violent, until hurting us and blinding us. The whole town drags itself —poles, trees, peoples, streets— to the shores of this stream of freshness and sea breezes. In the oven of the summer, fuming are the houses, of bread dough, and are scorching underneath. You don't come to my side anymore. A sexton hour turned off the sun with a willow's reed. And six bell strokes of steel: —Ite missa est— they said, simply, ritually, machinally. Now the sultriness is over, the being quiet, the lockedup annoyance, the inevitable shadow of this four-hour mass.

Martín Adán (left) and José Carlos Mariátegui (seated). Lima, circa 1928.

Colophon

For the publication of this book I am a little responsible, but like with all my responsibilities, I accept and assume this one with no reservations. Awakened on a school desk, this novel peeked out for the first time to the public from the windows of Amauta, three wide Inca trapezoids like the ones in Tampuctocco, from where the future is being measured by those who tomorrow will depart to its conquest. Martín Adán is not properly avant-garde, he is not revolutionary, he is not indigenist. He is a character invented by himself, whose birth I have testified, but of whose existence we have yet no other proof than his writings. Ramón's author is subsequent to his creature, against all biological laws and against all logical laws` of cause and effect. The folios of the novel were already written a long time before the necessity of giving them an author would produce that conciliation between the Genesis and Darwin that his name attempts. They constituted an adolescent and clandestine literature, paradoxically sheltered in the idyllic lap of the Social Action of Youth.[51] Moreover, humorously, Martín Adán calls himself reactionary, clerical and civilist. But his evident heresy, his contumacious skepticism, contradict him. The reactionary is always passionate. Skepticism is now demo-bourgeois[52], as it was aristocratic, when the bourgeois were believers and the aristocrats were encyclopedist and Voltairean. If Civilism is now capable only of heresy, it means that it's not capable of reaction. And I believe that the heresy of Martín Adán has this scope; and because of this, I

---

51. *Asociacion Social de la Juventud (ASJ).* Catholic youth associacion founded in 1926, whose mission was to promote cultural and sports activities, as well as social voluntary work. Estuardo Nuñez and Martín Adán were reluctant members, more interested in the association's modern game room than in its social activities. Adán's relations with Mariátegui's socialist milieu and the publication of excerpts from *The Cardboard House* in the leftist magazine *Amauta* created a small polemics with the neo-Catholics, which resulted in the separation of Adán from the association. *See. ed. Sosnowski, Saul. Lectura Critica de la Literatura Americana. Biblioteca Ayacucho. Venezuela, 1997. pp.419-420.*

52. Abbreviation for "democratic-bourgueois". The term appers frequently in Mariátegui's writings as an euphemism for the middle upper class represented by the politics of Civilism in Perú.

have hastened to register it as a sign. Without a doubt, Martín Adán doesn't worry about the political factors that, without him knowing it, decide his literature. Behold, nonetheless, a novel that would not have been possible before the Billinghurst experiment, the "Colonida" insurrection, the decadence of Civilism, the July 4th revolution and the public works of the Foundation.[53] I don't mean the technique, the style, but the subject, the content. A young man from a great family, measured, intelligent, Cartesian, reasonable like Martín Adán, would have never expressed himself disrespectfully of so many formerly respectable things; he wouldn't have denounced Ramón's aunt in such lively and plastic terms, a vacationer and resident of Barranco, and he wouldn't have taken her out to the public in a bobble stitch robe, solicitous, estival and intimate, with her cat and her little black maid; he wouldn't have failed to ask Esq. José de la Riva Agüero or Dr. Luis Varela Orbegoso for a foreword, nor would he have failed to show himself a little doctoral and universitary, with a thesis full of quotes about Esq. Felipe Pardo and Esq. Clemente Althaus, or any other Esq. Felipe or Esq. Clemente of our literature. His own

[53] For a detailed account of these events and Mariátegui's position regarding them, we must refer to his landmark study on Peruvian reality. *Mariátegui, Jose Carlos. Seven interpretive essays on Peruvian reality. University of Texas Press. 1988.*

parents would not have committed the temerarious imprudence of enrolling him in a German school from where he had to get, along with a few decals of Herr Oswald Teller, a certain scrupulous consideration for eighteenth-century science and its reconditely liberal theories, Protestant and progressive. Had he grown up some years before, Martín Adán would have been educated at the Recollects School or with the Jesuits, with different consequences. His faithful enrollment in the classes of a German lyceum corresponds to an epoch of capitalist growth, of anti-colonial demagogy, of neo-Gothic crumbling, of teaching the Saxon languages and the multiplication of commerce academies. An epoch vaguely prepared by Dr. Villarán's speech against liberal professionals, by Dr. Víctor Maúrtua's speech on material progress and the economic factor, and by Oscar Víctor Salomón's conferences, in Hyde Park, on foreign capital; but concretely, socially, materially and politically represented by Leguía-ism[54], the urbanizations, the asphalt, the nouveau riches, the Country Club, etc... The literature of Martín Adán is avant-garde, because it couldn't be otherwise, but Martín Adán himself is not yet completely so. The good old Anatole France, inveterate corrupter of minors, spoiled his innocence with those books of melodic prose, in which everything,

54. cf. note 33, p. 93

even cynicism and obscenity, has so much composure, erudition and classicism. And Anatole France is nothing but a demo-bourgeois of Paris, deliberately disenchanted, professionally skeptical, but full of an unlimited hope in the future; a petit bourgeois from the Seine, who since his youth produced the impression of being excessively and habitually old —an old man for comfort and a sedentary spirit—. Martín Adán still is in the Anatolian station, although he is already beggining to deny these books that initiated him in heresy and in skepsis. In his style, ordered and elegant, without wrinkles or shreds, one recognizes an absolutely classical taste. In some of the pages of *The Cardboard House* there are at times even a certain Azorinean listlessness. And not even in the most recent pages does one finds hallucinations or a suprarealistic pathos. Martín Adán is from the lineage of Cocteau and Radiguet more than from the lineage of Morand and Giradoux. In literature it happens to him as it does in school: he cannot help but get getting good achievement grades. His disorder is previously ordered. All his paintings, all his prints, are truthful, plausible, true. In *The Cardboard House* there is a schema of a biography of Barranco, or better, of its vacationers. If the biography turns out to be humoristic, it's not Martín Adán's fault, but rather Barranco's. Martín Adán has not invented Ramón's aunt or her robe, or her little black girl; everything he describes does exist. It has the essential conditions of the classic. His work is classical, rational, balanced, even though it may not seem so. One feels him classical, even to the extent in which he is anti-romantic. In the form he sometimes betrays the ascendant of Eguren; but not in the spirit. In Martín Adán, the imaginer is a bit Egurenian, but only the imaginer. Anti-romantic —up until the moment in which we write these lines, as journalists say— Martín Adán presents himself as always reluctant to adventure. "I will not kidnap you for anything in the world. I need you to go by your side wishing to kidnap you. Woe to the one who realizes his desire!" "Christian pessimism, Catholic pragmatism that poetically sublimates and comforts itself with words from Ecclesiastes". My love for adventure, it's probably what separates me from Martín Adán. The desire of the adventurous man is always unsatisfied. Every time it's realized, it's reborn bigger and more vicious. And when one walks at night next to a beautiful woman, one must always be ready for the rapture. Some readers will find in this book a denial of my words. They will think that the publication of The Cardboard House at the age of nineteen is an adventure. It may seem so, but it is not. I attest that Martín Adán has taken all his precautions. He publishes a book whose success is totally assured. And, nonetheless, he publishes it in a limited edition, before facing the public and the critics in a major edition. A purebred writer and artist, his appearance has the consensus of unanimity plus one. He is so eclectic and heretical, that he reconciles us all in a theosophically cosmic and monistic synthesis. I could not have saluted his arrival except in my own way: finding in his literature a corroboration of my agitator theses. That is why, although I didn't want to write more than a few lines, I have begotten a long paragraph, like the editorials of Dr. Clemente Palma. If it occurs to Martín Adán to attribute it to the poor Ramón, like his Underwood Poems, he will have achieved a more difficult reconciliation than that of Genesis and Darwin.

José Carlos Mariátegui

Martín Adán (Lima, 1908 - 1985), pseudonym of Ramón Rafael de la Fuente Benavides, was a Peruvian poet and writer whose body of work is notable for its experimentalism and metaphysical depth. His breakthrough novel, The Cardboard House, redefined the possibilities of narrative for his contemporaries and has remained a substantial influence for many generations of Latin American writers. He is one of the most celebrated Peruvian poets of the 20th century. His work in poetry was twice awarded the National Poetry Prize (Perú, 1946, 1961) and the Peruvian National Literature Prize in 1976.

José Garay Boszeta (Lima, 1985) is a writer, translator and language laborer, born and raised in Lima, Perú. He studied programs in Economics and Philosophy at the National University of San Marcos in Lima. His work in translation aims to reevaluate Latin American narratives and restore their historical content for English speaking audiences around the world. His current projects include the translation of the works of José María Eguren and Martín Adán, among others. He currently lives in Dallas, Texas with his wife, Erin and their dog, Willow.

Dulzorada